Praise for
Blue Sky Morning

"A brave story on overcoming adversity and reclaiming the life you were meant to live."
—Kary Oberbrunner, Author of *ELIXIR Project, Day Job to Dream Job, The Deeper Path*, and *Your Secret Name*

"Maier takes us on a journey around the world and illustrates the power that a person has to control their own destiny. This is a beautifully written tale that will leave you inspired."
—Cliff Ravenscraft, The Podcast Answer Man

"This is an engaging and encouraging journey recounted with beautiful imagery, and lasting insight."
—S.G. Savage, Author of *Lydia's League of Angels Series*

Blue Sky Morning

Blue Sky Morning

An Inward Journey
Around the World

CHRISTINE MAIER

This is a work of fiction.
All characters, organizations, and events portrayed in this novel
are products of the author's imagination or altered reality.

Printed in the United States

Published by Author Academy Elite
P.O. Box 43, Powell, OH 43035

www.AuthorAcademyElite.com

Paperback ISBN: 978-1-64085-034-7

Hardcover ISBN: 978-1-64085-036-1

Ebook ISBN: 978-1-64085-035-4

Library of Congress Control Number: 2017908007

For Dr. Bertram Bromberg, whom I never got to
thank for giving me a chance in life.

And for my mother and father,
who taught me how to use that chance.

Note to Reader

At the start of each chapter I added a flashback of Emily's life before the beginning of the main narrative. This was done because I found Emily really boring in the first chapter. I decided to add a flashback of the accident to make it more interesting. It worked so well that I added a flashback to each chapter, except for the last. The nineteen flashbacks are as real as Emily is.

The world is a beautiful place, even when the sky is gray and crying tears in the form of rain. But the journey of life tells us that sometimes we need a day with a bright blue sky to remember how beautiful the world is and that anything is possible.

Chapter 1

We were driving to the Hamptons on a Friday night, cruising along the Long Island Expressway. My college roommate and best friend, Eve, and I were finally having a girls' weekend away. Since we started our careers a few years ago, it had become harder and harder to find time to spend together.

Eve was a doctor living in New Jersey, and I was a lawyer working at a law firm in New York City. Life was good for both of us. We didn't see each other nearly enough, but we finally found a weekend to relax in a friend's summer rental. Just the two of us on a beach catching up like old times. The weather was still warm and humid, the sun low in the sky. It was the perfect beginning to the weekend.

The deep orange of the setting sun was a glimmer in my rear-view mirror. Miley Cyrus, Eve, and I were screaming, "I came in like a wrecking ball." When the black SUV swerved into my lane from the left, I didn't have time to react. I just felt the jolt to my body as I tried to control the car. I heard the screeching of tires and watched the world spin by like a movie on fast-forward. But mostly I remember the crunching of metal and the moment of complete silence when the car finally stopped.

That silence was shattered by Eve screaming my name. I tried to answer, but then everything went black.

I'm thinking about the same thing today that I've been pondering for the past few days. How did I get to this point in life? What thirty-one-year-old in the prime of her career decides to quit her job and travel the world? It seemed like a perfectly rational decision at the time. I wasn't enjoying my job, which made me question my career. The friends I had made along the way had mostly faded away since the accident a year and a half ago. There wasn't much keeping me at home anymore.

I'm a planner, and this was never part of my plan, but neither was the accident. I'm learning that sometimes a plan needs to change. Now the only plan I have is to travel around the world for the next six months. At this moment I find myself in the car headed to the airport. Plan or no plan, I wonder if this is the stupidest and most irresponsible decision of my life. I have money in the bank, hopefully enough to last the whole trip and a few weeks after while I settle back into my job when I return. If I still have my job, or even want it. I've set a budget for each stop, but who knows how accurate it will be, or what unexpected expenses will come up along the way. And as for my job, well, I guess that's not exactly a sure thing either.

"Emily." Mom's voice pulls me from my thoughts, and I realize we've arrived at JFK Airport.

"Oh, we're here." This trip is happening so quickly now. I couldn't even get a reprieve from the madness in my head by sitting in traffic. Nope, no traffic when you need it. If I were going to see a Broadway show, there would be traffic. I see my mother out of the corner of my eye, I notice the tender look of love in her eyes, fortunately no pity, and definitely no suspicion that she should take me to get checked out by a psychiatrist instead of dropping me off at an airport.

"Emily, you'll be fine. Stop overthinking it. You'll be back in a few months, and if you want to come home early, you can, or you can stay longer if you manage your money well. We'll all miss you, but you need to take some time for yourself." Now there's that hint of pity in her eyes. That's Mom, though, supportive of whatever she thinks will get me out of my funk.

After a year and a half, I can't blame her. I'm tired of the funk too, which I guess is why I'm leaving. By funk I mean depressed blob of lifelessness.

Mom and Dad are a sweet couple from Long Island. Dad works in the city and is nearing retirement; he's in the final stages of saving for it. Mom was a stay-at-home mom until my sister and I went to school. Then she got a secretary job at a doctor's office and was a member of the PTA until we graduated from high school. She still works at the same job. Their goal is to be snowbirds and spend half their time in sunny Florida and half here in New York to be close to my sister and me.

They are wonderful, loving parents, and after the accident they let me stay at their house while I recovered and settled back into life. My parents hadn't had kids at home for years, so it was interesting being together again. It was good to reconnect with them as an adult, but it's also time for me to reclaim my independence. No matter how much I tried, I never quite got my footing, and I really have no idea what I want to do with the rest of my life. About nine months ago, when I was in a bad place mentally, I decided to leave New York for a trip around the world.

Mom and I hug, say, "I love you." She sneaks twenty dollars into my hand as a parting gift and tells me to be careful. All the stuff your mom would do and say at the airport before you take a weeklong vacation to a tropical island with fruity drinks. Except I've barely recovered from the accident and I will be away at least six months. With the twenty dollars, I can afford one fruity drink.

I head into the terminal and go straight for the departure area for British Airways elite customers. Inside, it's almost serene. Unlike the rest of the airport, it's spacious, with a higher ceiling, more glass, and more openness. The furnishings are nicer, the volume is lower, and there are fewer people. The friendly staff adds to the relaxed atmosphere. It's almost serene enough to calm my nerves.

Almost.

By the time I cross the departure area and get to the check-in desk, my legs are so wobbly I wonder if they will carry me to the counter. As I'm called to the next agent, with a shaking hand I give her the boarding pass I printed this morning along with my passport. I wish I could blame the accident for the shaking, but I know it's my nerves. After working as a lawyer for years, I used to be excellent at hiding my emotions, particularly my nerves. The other lawyers in my office used to joke that I had titanium nerves, but I lost the ability to hide my emotions after the accident.

"Good evening, Miss Taylor. I see you'll be on Flight 116 nonstop to London/Heathrow, departing at 8:15 this evening. We have you assigned to seat 63B on the upper deck in Club World. Do you have any bags to check?"

I have just one medium-size suitcase that will carry all my stuff for the next six months. I packed it, then repacked it a dozen times in the past few weeks to make sure I could fit everything I needed to take. "One," is all I manage to say to the agent.

The joys of flying in business class include the cheerful and helpful staff that completely ignore my shaking hands and tentative voice. After checking my bag and adding an orange "PRIORITY" tag to it, Little Miss Cheerful informs me the flight will board at 7:15 and points me in the direction of the lounge where I can have dinner and schedule a massage.

Before the accident, my career as a lawyer had me traveling almost half the year, taking flights all over the United States and staying in nice hotels. Another lawyer at the firm taught me some tricks for earning points and miles for travel so I have enough to fund most of the flights on this trip and some of my hotels. When I was collecting those points, I thought I would use them for nice vacations and maybe a honeymoon. Instead, I'm using them to escape the life I thought was perfect but discovered wasn't at all.

I've been in some lounges during all that travel, but this one is the grandest. Usually I just get some light snacks and drinks; this one offers a gourmet dinner. I also usually had some people to talk to. Instead, I'm in this beautiful setting by myself, questioning this decision and all the ones I will have to make over the next six months. As I am eating, I wonder what was the all-time low point in the last year and a half that brought me here. I don't want to delve too deeply into that yet: there are too many possibilities.

Six months of traveling around the world sounded great in my head. But now that it's happening, I'm not sure I'm ready for it. Even though I've traveled all over the United States for work and the rare vacation, I've never left the country. My vacations before the accident mostly consisted of going to a resort hotel on a beach where I attempted to avoid working; my trip around the world is best described as insanity. I've never had to worry about passports, currency exchange, foreign languages.

It probably doesn't help that my sister, Jessica, made me watch a series of horror movies about travel: *Hostel*, *The Descent*, *An American Werewolf in London*, and *Taken*. I drew the line at *Snakes on a Plane*. She said she was trying to help me get over my fear of getting sick in another country and not being able to communicate with the doctor. I also might have expressed a concern about not finding any food to eat. I can be a picky eater at times, and I could only pack so many granola bars. Jess thought a fear of being kidnapped and killed was healthier than worrying about food and coming down with a cold.

I've lived in New York City for years so I'm not exactly a stranger to crime. I haven't been a direct target, but in a big city crime happens around you–to a friend, colleague, or family member. Being or knowing a victim is inevitable. The best you can do is learn from their mistakes. Over the years I learned a lot of tricks to avoid being a crime statistic–the areas to stay away from, behaviors that make you an easy target. Being away from New York is different. I won't know all the areas to avoid or know the cultural behaviors for the places I will visit. With long hair, blue eyes, and particularly white skin, I know I'll look like a tourist in some of the places I want to see. And there's also the scar on my face.

I finally get a break from my overactive brain when it's time for my massage. The dim lighting and soft music in the spa are soothing. Even my hands stop shaking by the time the masseuse, Jennifer, brings me to the treatment room. Jennifer's voice is calm as she directs me where to store my bags. As I start to relax, my brain starts to slow down. Then Jennifer asks about medical conditions she needs to be aware of and suddenly my breathing becomes more shallow and my mouth gets dry as I list my medical concerns. I start by telling her I broke several bones in my left leg and ankle. None of my injuries faze Jennifer. She continues with her soft voice and explains exactly how she'll adjust the massage for my comfort.

Jennifer is amazing, taking away my anxiety in fifteen minutes. I'm half asleep by the time she finishes, my muscles a little softer, my brain a little clearer. Maybe I should skip the trip and hire Jennifer as a permanent masseuse. As I slowly peel myself out of the chair, I ask Jennifer how she does it. Her response is so simple that I almost can't process it.

"I love what I do. While some might think being a masseuse isn't an exciting job, I get a reward with each person I meet. Every person who steps into my treatment room is a chance for me to make someone else's life better. Some are fighting stress at work or home; others are anxious to fly. My job isn't just to loosen their muscles–it's to help them leave this room in a better place. When I do that, I go home satisfied and excited to come back to work."

I stare at her for a minute before thanking her. "I've worked with a lot of very smart people. I don't think any of them could have described their jobs so eloquently."

She has a beaming smile as she escorts me out of the spa so I can catch my flight. As I walk to the gate, I think about what Jennifer said. As a lawyer I've spent most of my time writing detailed, technical contracts that one or two people would read. I work with a lot of intelligent people. I like to think I was one. I also liked to think I was helping people on some higher level; however, I never got to see a real smile of thanks from a client. I was paid well, but it was rare that I went home and toasted myself to making someone's life better.

When I booked my ticket for this flight, I chose the Boeing 747—the infamous two-story plane—business class seat in the upper deck. I wanted to see if it felt any different from a regular one-story plane. The first thing I notice after climbing the stairs to my seat is that this area is much smaller than the first level. The second thing I notice is that the seats face each other; each pair of seats has one facing forward and one facing the back of the plane. Although the seats are technically next to each other, the configuration has you facing someone else, just slightly off to the side. It's creepy. I really didn't want to have to stare at someone the whole flight. It's not that I don't like people, but I feel like there's some social requirement that we talk, and the more we sit staring at each other, the more time we have to imagine a story about the other person.

While boarding, I had felt my phone vibrate but ignored it, until now. The texts make me smile. Eve and Jess would never forget to wish me well.

Text from Jessica:
I'm so excited for you, have fun. Don't do anything I wouldn't do!

Text to Jessica:
Not much of a standard is it? Miss you. Take care of M&D.

Text from Eve:
GOOD LUCK! I'll miss you and stop freaking out! Love you!

Text from Eve:
Is your seatmate cute? If he is chat him up. It's time to do something crazy!

Text to Eve:
Just got on the plane. No seatmate yet, but the seats face each other. I guess I can't hide ACK!

Text to Eve:
Love you too.

Shortly after sitting, a middle-aged male in a suit with salt and pepper hair sits next to and facing. He reminds me of a stuffy conservative executive. I give a polite half smile and try to concentrate on examining my British Airways gift bag. Along with an eye mask and ear plugs, it has a toothbrush, toothpaste, and a selection of fancy creams to help freshen up at the end of the flight.

My strategy doesn't work long, Mr. Stuffy eventually wants to make small talk. He starts with the usual questions: Where are you going? Business or pleasure? I am polite but give short answers, attempting to avoid a longer conversation. I don't think even Eve would suggest I spend much time talking to him, so no guilt there. My short answers don't deter him, though, and he asks how I got the scar on my cheek.

During the accident, a piece of glass cut the left side of my face. I have a light but noticeable scar starting below my eye and running several inches down my cheek, ending near my mouth. It's not my worst scar, but it was the one that is the hardest to hide. I had great reconstruction and even got second opinions, but there's little hope of removing it.

I look down briefly at the creams on my lap before mumbling that it happened in a car accident. I do not look in his direction long: I am used to pitying stares after that answer and having to pretend I don't want to cry. I shouldn't have worried. Instead of staring, he offers me a business card for his Manhattan plastic surgery office. I'm shocked, so shocked that I take the card and thank him.

After that, I pull out the menu and pretend to read. It isn't long before the passenger from across the aisle catches my eye. I thought I had gotten better at hiding from people. I was wrong.

"Excuse me; I heard what that man said to you. Don't listen to him. He's rude. You're a beautiful woman." Then she winks at me.

I am stunned and feel an urge to hug her and cry at the same time. I settle for thanking her with a smile. Then I go back to my fake menu reading and see the new text messages on my phone.

Text from Eve:
```
Is it a he? Is he cute?
```

Text to Eve:
```
Older woman. You'll have to find another fantasy.
```

Text from Eve:
```
Back to the advice of Tim McGraw—go skydiving.
```

Text to Eve:
```
Right after you get on a plane and come visit me. We
        should be taking off soon, toodles!
```

Text from Eve:
```
That was mean! You must be really freaked out. Don't worry
I'll forgive you by the time you land.
```

One little lie to Eve won't hurt. But she's right—I was mean. Eve lived a few blocks from where a plane crashed shortly after 9/11. She's afraid to fly now. I stopped mentioning it after she got angry a couple times. I think she's trying to get me to do all the things she'll never do. Meanwhile, my biggest goal now is to do a little research and find out how I'm going to make my way to my London hotel without getting lost.

Shortly after takeoff, Mr. Stuffy puts up a small wall between our seats, and I once again have my privacy from his rudeness. Because I had dinner in the lounge, I pass on the meal. Instead, I play with my seat, test out the different positions, and flip through the channels on the onboard TV. Eventually I put my seat in the lie-flat position, snuggle up with my blanket and pillow, and fall asleep to the clinking of dishes as dinner is served in the cabin.

Chapter 2

I t hurts. Everything hurts. I try to open my eyes. The lights are too bright and I squish them closed again.

Beep.

Beep.

Beep.

"No, Eve, she's still asleep."

Beep.

"You should really go home and rest. You look tired."

Beep.

"Mom," I try to say, but no words come out.

"Eve?" It comes out as a whisper. I'm trying to open my eyes, but they won't cooperate.

Beep.

Beep.

The beeping is faster now.

"Emily? How are you?" It's my mother's voice.

Beep.

"Maaa," I croak.

Beep.

Beep.

"Can you open your eyes?" It's Mom's voice again.

The lights are dim this time when I open my eyes, the first thing I see is a clock that looks like it's from a Tim Burton movie. When I finally find Mom's face she has a halo of light around her head. I try to move my mouth, but I'm not certain my muscles work. "Where?" is all I'm able to ask.

Beep.

"Go get the nurse," I hear my mother say.

Beep.

"Emily, you're in the hospital. You were in a car accident."

"Hurts," I groan.

"I know, dear, but you're going to be okay. You have a button in your hand, you can press it when it hurts." I feel a plastic thing, and with a little effort I find the button and press it.

"Eve?" I thought I heard her in the room.

"She's okay. She said she might come visit later."

I remember hearing her voice. I thought she was here.

The beeping increases.

"Dag?"

"Dad just stepped out. He'll be back in a few minutes," she answers.

"No, Dagoberrrr?" I try to enunciate my boyfriend's name.

"Dagobert is working. I'm sure he'll come by later."

I want to ask more, but I feel a heavy darkness take over and pull me back into a slumber while the beeping in the background slows down to a calm rhythm.

I wake to the sound of breakfast dishes. The smell of warm bread wafts through the airplane cabin and gives me a small incentive to open my eyes. The lights are dim and people are just starting to stir. As I continue to focus, I notice the flight attendant in her blue suit is still a few seats away, and I opt to make my way to the restroom before breakfast.

As I approach, I see the female passenger I spoke to the night before. She greets me with a friendly smile and whispers, "Good morning. I'm Alma. Did you sleep well?"

Although I am still groggy, I manage a smile. "A few hours. Thank you. You?" Before she has a chance to answer, one of the accordion doors opens and Alma disappears behind it.

After freshening up in the bathroom with the goodies from the airline bag, I am ready for what turns out to be the best airplane breakfast I've ever had: a smoothie, coffee, eggs, fruit, bread, and pastries. While I am eating, Alma once again strikes up conversation with me, asking me where I am headed. I tell her that my hotel is near Green Park and that I am just going to explore today, probably take a hop-on-and-off bus so I can get an overview of the city.

"Oh, good. And that's a nice easy trip on the Tube to the hotel for you," she responds.

The Tube? I hadn't considered the Tube. A friend had mentioned taking the Tube, but I usually take a taxi to and from the airport. Of course, I usually have an expense account to cover it. Besides, that I'm taking this trip is enough adventure for day one. Isn't it?

"I was just going to take a taxi to the hotel. I would hate to get lost my first morning here," I eventually admit. Why am I telling all this to a stranger?

"Don't take a taxi. They're terribly expensive and much slower this time of day. Even my daughter will take the Tube with her little ones to avoid the traffic. The Tube will only cost a few pounds and it's very easy." Alma continues about how the underground might be dirty but it's safe and the best way to get around the city. Listening to her I have a sense of déjà vu. I'm sure that's what I sound like when I tell people to take the subway in New York City, even though I avoid the subway whenever I can.

"Is it really that much to take a taxi? I figured after not getting much sleep on the plane, being in a new city, and with my luggage it would be easier to take a taxi." I have visions of a London black cab driving me around and giving me a mini tour of London on the way. I am aware of the lack of traffic in the vision, but I ignore it.

"I suppose it is easier," Alma relents.

Before she can continue, my brain-to-mouth filter stops working, and I start to babble. "What about crime on the Tube or a terrorist attack? Aren't we supposed to be extra vigilant these days? I'll also miss the adventure of taking a London cab and getting a mini-tour. How much money would I really save?" I think I hear Alma sigh. She seems sure she's lost the argument and that I'm going to spend too much money on a cab I don't need to take.

"It will save you about forty pounds, and it's really much easier than sitting in traffic. No, you won't get to see the city on the Tube, but there is plenty of time for that. As for the rest, you can't spend time worrying. Of course, be careful, but you can't let fear dictate what you do. I'm guessing you're from New York City and you're not afraid there. Why be scared in London? The Tube may be old, but it's well cared for and there are lifts in many stations. You'll find it's much easier than you think."

She's right, and that's annoying. I might not like the subway, but being afraid never stopped me from riding it. Forty pounds? That would feed me for a day, or cover a tour and maybe a couple of frozen drinks with umbrellas. There's so much I could do with forty pounds. I could have planned this much better had I not dismissed the Tube so quickly before the trip.

"You can still take your London cab while you're here. Be daring—live a little. It's the oldest metro system in the world. You must ride it at some point. Why not today?" Alma's mood changed quickly. I suspect I've become her pet project for the rest of the flight.

Alma explains how to get from the airport to the hotel, which lines to take and how to navigate the system.

Still frustrated, but convinced by her simple directions, the conversation transitions to Alma giving me tips on things to do and see in London. I make some mental notes, but I know I'll forget most of her advice by the time I leave the airport. As we disembark the plane, I follow Alma, making the walk a little less lonely. It's a nearly desolate area of the airport, except for the people from our flight. I feel like we're walking through a glass and steel maze as we go down escalators and take a train to the main part of the airport. Here Alma and I part ways because she went to a UK entry line. Suddenly I'm alone again, in a long line. I people watch as I shuffle my papers and check and recheck my landing card.

Everyone seems bored and tired, their faces impassive and their legs shifting as they wait. Even the people traveling in groups don't talk. In the silence of my head and without my guide Alma, I'm back to the idea of taking the taxi. It just seems so much easier.

Once I make it to the front of the line, I find it's amazingly easy to get into England. I answer a few questions—the purposed of my trip, how long I'm away, where I am staying—and get my passport stamped. As I collect my bags, I run into Alma again. She walks with me for a few minutes before pointing me in the direction of the Tube. There's no escaping it now. I must either take the Tube or tell Alma I'm frightened.

The latter option is tempting.

We say our good-byes, and I thank her for her help as she leaves to meet her daughter. I go where she points and buy my ticket. I cross my fingers and carefully follow the signs to the station. It's not a long walk, and the wait for a train is only a few minutes.

The first thing I notice when the train pulls into the station is how small it looks; the subway cars are much bigger in New York City. Inside, the seats are a dark-blue fabric with red designs, a step up from the plastic seats at home. It's funny that Alma would mention that the Tube is dirty. Compared to the subway, this seems like a sparking gem.

As we sit in the station, the train slowly fills with passengers from the airport with all their luggage, which is not a common sight in New York City, a reminder of just how far away I am. The train car is almost full by the time they close the doors, and we're whisked away to London.

After getting out of the airport, we ride above ground. The views are different from home with smaller houses and more trees. It's not long before we go back underground, and I focus on the people inside the train. With each stop we slowly lose passengers with luggage and pick up new passengers headed into the city for the day. It's an interesting mix, and I notice that no matter what people wear, the blank stare common on the subway in New York City is also here in London.

As Alma promised, I arrive at the Green Park station fifty minutes later. I exit the train with several other passengers and try to stop to see where to go, but the herd of passengers moves me to the left. I shuffle along with the herd of people until I find signs for the elevator, or the lift as they call it here.

Once outside the station I take a moment to marvel at my first glimpse of London. On one corner is the Ritz Carlton, on another there's a giant park, and the opposite side of the street is lined with shops. As I stand gawking at the sites, I'm bumped by a business man. I chastise myself as I realize I have become one of the annoying tourists I complain about at home. I quickly move out of the way to check where I'm going. Looking at a London map while on the Tube is not the same as standing on the actual street. I pull out my guidebook and find the map that I dog-eared with my hotel marked on it. I'm thrown off by the cars and busses going the wrong direction on the street. I make a mental note to *always* check both ways before crossing. I don't want to get hit by a car.

When I start to make my way to the hotel, I notice a hop-on-and-off bus near the train station. After I drop my bags off at the hotel, I can come back here for a tour. As I walk, I take note of food options. Starbucks and Pret a Manger probably aren't cheap, but will work until I find a grocery store. I need to buy myself some food for breakfast and snacks. I'm staying in a nice hotel and I know breakfast alone will drain my savings, an expense I can't afford.

As I get closer to the hotel, the area becomes more residential, a surprising change since it's such a short walk from such a busy area. I'm relieved when the hotel clerk tells me my room is ready even though it's hours before check-in time. I appreciate the chance to freshen up after traveling overnight.

When I get to my room, I'm shocked. It's small and everything is different. There's a twin bed, which I've never seen in a hotel. I noticed this in the description when I booked the room, but it didn't register at the time. The fixtures and furnishings are obviously all new and well cared for, but they're a bit unusual. They have clean lines, but the materials are different. Different types of wood, metals, and fabric. The desk, the countertops, the table, and chair all look smaller than at home.

I put my thoughts of the furnishings aside and sit on the bed for a moment. I take the opportunity to send messages home that I've arrived safely. Then I search for and download some maps to my phone, another task I should have done in New York but didn't. I thought the giant guidebook I bought for London would be more helpful. Instead, it's a 750-page beaming headlight telling people I'm a tourist.

The nerves of landing and finding my way to the hotel have me edgy, keeping me awake and alert. As I try to relax, the bed calls to me to lay down and rest. I know the first rule of adjusting to the time change is to stay up during the day and sleep at night. I survived on much less sleep while in school and working as a lawyer. I can do it here too. With that thought, I stand and open my suitcase to prepare myself to see London.

In the mirror, I take a moment to examine the scar on my face. While it's pretty straight across my cheek and near my lips, it's jagged and messier closer to my ear. The only help is that most of the bad part can be hidden with my hair if I style it right. After I arrange my hair to hide it, I bundle up and head outside.

It's a cloudy and chilly spring morning in London; once I'm ready, I pull my coat tighter. As I retrace my steps toward the Green Park Tube station, I stop in one of the shops I noticed earlier for a late-morning pastry. I can already feel myself getting hungry and don't want my day dictated by my stomach. Then I walk across the street toward the bus stop, thankful for the paint on the ground reminding me which way to look to avoid being a victim.

When I approach the bus stop, I either look very lost or like a tourist. I'm immediately met by several guys trying to sell me tickets. I have this feeling of being swarmed and eaten by their aggression. They're peppering me with prices, the benefit of some walking tour that I just missed and the river cruise I can still take. They shove brochures in my face and tell me how it's cheaper to buy a ticket for several days. All I can think is that I should have stayed in the hotel and taken a nap.

Chapter 3

After being trapped in bed for what feels like months, I manage to talk my mother into a field trip to the hospital gift shop. You know the saying, "It takes a village." Well, the village is certainly required to get me out of bed each day. The nurses and physical therapists insist on it to keep my body working. Soon they will want me to try to walk. Any muscle development I can do now will help later. The only difference today is that instead of going into a recliner chair, I sit in a wheelchair. The change in position is nice but awkward as I try to get comfortable.

When I'm finally settled in the wheelchair, I'm exhausted and wondering whether this is a bad idea. But the monotony of the last few weeks wears off as Mom starts to push me down the hall. The hospital becomes fascinating as we roll by the nurse's station and patient rooms with visitors coming and going. There's a little world going on outside my room, and I never realized it. As we get closer to the hospital lobby, the corridors get busier. I start to notice a few stares. Surely a person in a wheelchair is not a strange occurrence, even with a hospital gown and blanket. Maybe it's the scar on my face. I thought it looked better the last time I saw it. When was that, yesterday or the day before. With all the medicine I'm taking, I can't remember. I hope they're not staring at me because I'm ugly now, not that I would blame them.

I try to tell myself I'm just imagining it, until I see a little kid look straight at me and then huddle into her mother's leg to hide. It's unnerving to be on display like this, but my mother seems oblivious to their looks as she pushes me into the gift shop. Inside I glance through the magazines, ultimately leaving the fashion magazines and picking tabloid types that will serve as brain candy. Between the lack of interaction with people and all the medication they give me, I have the attention span of a fish; these are about all I can digest. As I sit reviewing which ones I want, I notice a couple of teenage girls giggling in the corner. When I look up, they are huddled together and one is pointing at me as they whisper. Their faces change to embarrassment once they notice me looking at them, and then they scurry out of the gift shop.

My mother seems oblivious to this incident too. I hand her two magazines and tell her I'm ready to go. Although she offers to walk me through the rest of the gift shop, I claim fatigue and need to go back to the room. When we make our way back through the corridors toward the elevators, I see the teenage girls again. One looks right at me as she whispers into her friend's ear. I look away and fight the tears that I feel are coming.

Later that day I wake to the nurse and my mother chatting about how busy the hospital is today. Apparently, it is the last day of some weird medical display in the lobby and it's attracted some extra visitors. The display of items that emergency room doctors have removed from patient body parts is being moved to another area of the hospital tonight. Maybe my mother will take me to see it another day because I missed it today when we went to the gift shop.

The more the men tell me about the different bus tour options I shouldn't miss, the more my heart rate increases and the fuzzier my head gets. I hear what they are saying, but I can't absorb or process any of it. The voices start to remind me of the adults in *Charlie Brown*, then the talking gets faster and more piercing. Do I want to do a walking tour and a Thames cruise? I have no idea, but it all sounds like things I should be doing. I feel like I'm watching myself from above as I pay the man with strange-looking bills. The transaction is so quick I'm not even sure if I paid him the right amount. The guy seemed okay. He wouldn't have tried to trick me, right? Ugh, why wouldn't he? I'm acting like the perfect mark. I'm not even sure what I bought. The man points in the direction of a bus and tells me it will be leaving in a few minutes.

I slowly walk to the bus in a haze, show my papers to the bus driver, and find a seat on the lower level. I stare out the window for a few minutes before I go through the papers in my hand. It looks like I spent most of my taxi savings on a forty-eight-hour pass. The pass covers different bus routes, walking tours, and a river cruise. I decide to look at it all later, after I relax and get settled. I stare out the window and watch the people come and go from the train station. As my body starts to relax, I have that clammy feeling you get after you've been sweating under layers of clothing on a cool day and end up almost shivering. Not a great way to start the day or my trip.

When I look at my watch, I realize the man and I have a different definition of a few minutes. I wait ten minutes for the bus to depart. In the meantime, the bus fills with a mix of tourists: couples, families, and singles. When the bus finally pulls away, it follows a route along Green Park, and the commentary tells us the history of the park, starting with its use as a burial ground for lepers.

It's not long until our first stop, a slightly more uplifting spot at the edge of Green Park, lined with war memorials. Out the opposite window I notice a Hard Rock Café. I can't remember whether I've ever eaten at a Hard Rock Café, but it's close to the hotel and is a familiar sight. I had a boss who told me that when he went to school in London, the only place to get a good burger was the Hard Rock Café. Perhaps I can test his theory while I'm here.

As the bus starts to move, the audio commentary goes on about the war memorials that I can barely see, leading me to move to the upper deck for better views. As we approach Marble Arch, we learn the history of Speakers' Corner, the epicenter of many revolts, where many speakers practiced their skill.

At a different time in my life this would be a fascinating spot to stop and listen to speeches and maybe even give my own. Of course, it's a romanticized vision for an American who never needed a speaker's corner. I have the virtue of using my degree in law to exercise my right to free speech often. After several years at the law firm, I finally achieved a level where I had some flexibility to work on projects that I enjoyed and cases where I felt like I could make a difference. Of course, that all changed after the accident: I got stuck with boring cases and fewer opportunities to make an impact. Maybe I should come back here. But who wants to listen to a bitter American complaining about life?

The commentary continues giving us the history of England, and the neighborhoods become nicer, more exclusive with fancy buildings and high-end shopping. There's a grandeur to the shops here unlike those at home. Beautiful archways and balconies line the street. It feels so regal compared to the canyon effect of New York City with the skyscrapers. I won't be doing much shopping. I can't afford it, and I have no need for fancy clothes and accessories while I'm traveling. Yet the atmosphere makes me yearn to return to a time when I would have enjoyed shopping along Regent Street.

It's not long before we arrive in Oxford Circus, the Times Square of London, which is a disappointment. It's got a giant billboard in it; otherwise, it's just a big square, but not Times

Square *big*. I was going to get off here to look around and see what's happening before the chaos of the evening comes. I assumed because Oxford Circus has been compared to Times Square that it would get crazy busy.

The bus continues through the theatre district and eventually to Trafalgar Square, which looks familiar from TV news of gatherings in London. What catches my interest is at the other end of Whitehall. Past the war memorials is the seat of the British government. The bus commentary reminds me that tours of Parliament must be booked in advance. Another thing I wanted to do. I mentally add booking a ticket there and visiting nearby Westminster Abby to my list of things I want to do. As we pass Big Ben, I think of that scene in *Vacation* where they get stuck in the traffic circle in London and Clark keeps pointing out Big Ben and Parliament. I finally chuckle about that silly scene and send a text message to Jessica that I am here.

As we make our way along the river, I realize I missed the stop where I could have picked up a river cruise. I need to pay more attention to what I'm doing and what I want to do. I seem to want to delay everything to later or another day, but my time here isn't endless. At least I got the forty-eight-hour pass so I can take advantage of the stops I've missed so far, which is all of them.

When we pass Buckingham Palace, I take a few quick pictures to send to Eve. She's a closet royal fanatic, and I know she's been waiting for me to send her a picture of something royal.

Fifteen minutes later the bus returns to the same place where I got on. I look at the map and realize the bus is restarting its route. I make my way to a guide on the bus, and he confirms I'm the idiot who stayed on the bus so long that the route is starting again. Except he says it a little nicer than that. He suggests I get off and wait for the bus for the other route to come, assuring me it won't be a long wait and that I won't get lost.

I follow his advice and hang my head as I gather my stuff and get off the bus. I am disappointed that over two hours have gone by, and while I've learned a few things about London, I've only been seeing the city from the upper deck of a bus. I came on this trip to experience more than a change of scenery, but that's about all I've done in my first few hours here. Not a good sign for how the next six months are going to be.

As I descend the steps I realize I'm hungry, though it's certainly not from all the work I've been doing today. I don't think sitting on the bus builds an appetite. I look around and realize I'm not far from the Hard Rock Café. I give in to temptation and decide to have lunch in the only restaurant I've noticed since I got to London.

I'm seated toward the back of the restaurant with no view of the street and I order a cheeseburger. When I reach into my bag I pull out an object and give the black-haired plastic woman a once-over. It's my going away gift from Eve, a doll replica of Eve, complete with removable white coat. I stare at her for a minute before putting her back in my bag. When I grab my cell phone, I notice all the missed messages from the real Eve, as well as my family.

Text to Eve:
I have a present for you already!
Look, it's Buckingham Palace!

Text from Eve:
Awesome, you're high up. Did you take that picture from the bus?

Text to Eve:
Maybe . . .

Text from Eve:
I'm waiting for the cool selfie you took with the ridiculous selfie stick your mother gave you.

Text to Eve:

That pic doesn't exist.

Text from Eve:
You have time still, I want a goofy selfie of you and Buckingham
Palace, not a boring crooked picture.

Eve is one of the few people in my life who pushed me to
do this trip. The other is my crazy Aunt Sloane, who is always
planning some exotic trip. Aunt Sloane is the one who started
the idea and who didn't think my itinerary was bold enough.

Before leaving, I book a tour of Parliament for the following day and head back out to the bus. Feeling a little bolder,
and pressured to be more adventurous, I get off at the first
stop, Harrods.

My stop at Harrods is mostly to get a picture that Eve will
appreciate, but will also satisfy my shopping craving. I decide
that since it's late, I don't need to spend too much time here.
But I'm here long enough to realize that Harrods is like no
other store I've been to before. I spend most of my time in the
loud but energetic food areas, picking up pastries and sweet
rolls I can eat over the next few days. It's not exactly cheap, but
the quality is good and the options eclectic to my American
tastes. What's more surprising, though, is how busy Harrods
is. I always thought it would be a tourist trap. However, I
didn't imagine there being so many tourists buying this much
stuff. It's almost as busy as Times Square on a Saturday night.

I get a selfie inside Harrods and send it to Eve while I wait
for the next bus. Hopefully that will shut her up for a while.

As the bus rolls through Notting Hill and Bakers Gate, we
see areas of the city that have been on TV and in movies over
the years, and it gives me a slight sense of familiarity. Soon
the bus starts to repeat the route I took in the morning, and
I realize I don't have many options left for the day. I vow to
plan better for tomorrow.

As we approach the Tower of London, again, the bus driver announces that the last river cruise of the day will be leaving shortly. Do I go on it or go back to the hotel? It only takes me a few seconds to decide. I gather my things and rush off the bus.

I stop quickly to take a few pictures of the Tower of London and then suddenly realize I don't know where the river cruise departs from. In my head the bus stop and the pier were right next to each other, but they are not. When I look around, there's no stream of people headed in any one direction. I ring my hands as I walk toward the water. It's a boat; it will be in the water, right?

Eventually I spot someone who looks like they work here and get pointed in the right direction. I speed walk toward the pier as fast as my legs will let me. I'm not sure how much time I have until the last boat departs.

I make it to the pier with a few minutes to spare and find myself a seat near a window. As the commentary tells us about the Tower of London, I start to drift off to sleep. I try to fight it, telling myself that the ride isn't long and I can go to sleep early tonight. The next thing I know we're docking at the end of the cruise. I'm still a little groggy when I make my way to the bus stop.

When the bus arrives at Buckingham Palace, I get off and take my selfie. It's the perfect setting with the sun starting to go down over London. After positioning my hair to cover my scar, I get up the courage to ask someone from the bus to take my picture. I make my way back to the hotel and send the picture to Eve before collapsing on the bed for the night.

I wake the following morning and the room is still dark, even though the shades are open. When I look harder I see the first rays of sunlight outside telling me it's just before sunrise. The first few minutes I'm awake everything feels so heavy; my limbs have sunk into the hard mattress and aren't eager to move.

Once I get my body moving, I find myself wide-awake, rested, and ready to begin the day. I take the extra time this morning to plan for the day and eat my Harrods breakfast. I want to take the walking tour this morning to see the Changing of the Guard in front of Buckingham Palace, then in the afternoon I'll visit Parliament and Westminster Abbey.

I decide to use the same tour bus to get around the city today since I've already paid for it. When I get bored with the bus's commentary about London, I can get off the bus and walk, which is what I do when I reach Regent Street. It's another cool and cloudy morning with rain expected in the afternoon, perfectly matching my plans for the day. I'll be indoors when the rain is expected.

Regent Street is even more impressive from the ground now that I have a chance to look more closely at the buildings that line the street. The intricate designs in the facades, the unique placement of the signs, and the commemorative plaques describing some of the buildings add to the unique flare. The walk gives me an opportunity to understand London better. I dodge people on their way to work on my window-shopping expedition. Most shops haven't opened yet. The hustle and bustle of London reminds me of home, with people rushing to work, the gym, shopping, errands.

Eventually I make my way to Trafalgar Square for a walking tour that will end with the Changing of the Guard. I thought we would just stand at Buckingham Palace and watch there. But our guide starts us at St. James Palace and then walks us to Buckingham Palace, so we can see the entire ceremony. Overall, the tour is interesting, but the best part is being around people, even if I barely speak to them and will never see them again. Just being with other human beings changes the feeling of the morning, makes me feel less isolated.

At the end of the tour, I take a black cab to Parliament. The cab isn't as exciting as I thought it would be, even though my driver is polite. He made sure I was dropped off in the right place, but doesn't explain much about the city. However, Parliament meets every expectation. I fall in love with the colorful windows, and ornately decorated period ceilings throughout the building.

Almost as impressive as Parliament, I visit Westminster Abbey next. I want to be excited that this is the location where monarchs are crowned and Prince William and Kate were married, but there is so much more love. With over 1,000 years of history, it has survived wars and hosted some of the greatest writers, and world leaders.

Towards the end of my tour of Westminster Abbey, jet lag starts to overtake my body. I planned to take a walking tour after, but I'm so exhausted that I settle on the evening bus tour of the city. I manage to fall asleep halfway through the evening loop. At the end of the evening I feel a small sense of accomplishment at all I got done in the day. Hopefully tomorrow will be even better.

Chapter 4

The phone rings as I enter my apartment. "Hello?"

"Hey, Em, glad I caught you. I can't make it to SCUBA tonight," Eve blurts in a single breath. Not surprising news. It's not the first time she's canceled plans at the last minute.

"No problem. Did you call the place? Will they give you your money back?"

"I didn't. I don't have time. Can you take care of that for me? I have to run."

She seems rushed so I tell her I'll take care of it and can barely say good-bye before she hangs up.

I have no time to be disappointed that both my boyfriend and best friend have canceled SCUBA lessons on me at the last minute. Instead, I change into comfortable clothes and rush out the door so I can make it on time. I don't want to become another last-minute cancellation. I could be mad at the two of them, but I'm sure I've done the same to them.

I sign into class and talk with another girl who is here on her own. I'm going to need a buddy, might as well make one now so I don't have to deal with the awkward moment where you don't have a partner and the instructor pairs everyone. Kathy is alone because her boyfriend is already SCUBA certified and they're going to Australia in a few months and want to dive together. I'm relieved. I know Kathy is invested in being here, and she's cool, so I'll have a friend for the duration of the class and maybe even afterward. When it's time to get ready to enter the water, the instructor helps each of us with equipment. Instead of standing around waiting, I help the group pair off for the class.

Once in the water, we all stay in our pairs and follow the instructions to test our equipment and practice the skills we learned during the lecture. The first moment we're allowed to sink down under the water is amazing. Normally I would have to fight to stay under like this, but now we just remain down. We're kept on our knees with our partners to test equipment; I feel like I can walk on the floor of the pool for miles. It's so peaceful, silent, and calm being underwater like this. There's an occasional sound that leaks through from the outside or from another diver; otherwise I feel like I'm on another planet, far away from my Manhattan apartment.

When the alarm goes off, everything feels so stiff, it takes a minute to realize I'm not in my soft, plush bed, but a hard hotel room bed in London. As the disorientation fades, I remember that today I am going to visit a castle, Stonehenge, and Bath. I was so excited when I booked this day trip a few weeks ago. My body and brain are not on the same page, though. I'm not sure if it's fatigue from the day before or a bad dream during the night, but I struggle to get out of bed. When I look out the window, I see that it's a dreary day, which aggravates the lingering pain I still have in my leg.

I manage to get myself to the tour's pick-up point with only a minute or two to spare. A fresh-faced, slim, blonde-haired girl shows up moments later and asks me if I'm taking a tour too. It turns out this Tinkerbell look-a-like is Clara and she will be on my tour. While waiting for the bus, I find out she's from Melbourne, Australia, and is on a sabbatical. I try to hide the scar on my face with my hair while we talk. She continues to talk to me after the bus arrives and our guide starts telling us about the plan for the day. Clara even makes friends with a mother and daughter across the aisle of our minibus.

We quiet as our guide tells us the history of the royal family on our way to Windsor Castle, our first stop of the day. I try to make a few notes in my journal as we go, but quickly forget the facts and quit. The same as I did with my journal the last two days. Instead, I sit and listen to the stories of the British monarchs since William the Conqueror.

When we arrive, the castle is even more majestic than I had imagined. The castle towers above the superb grounds with its lush green grass and tree-lined walks. It looks like nothing I've ever seen, and that's before we even make it to the parking lot. When I look at the hill we need to climb to the castle, I wonder how soldiers and servants made the walk, let alone how I will. I tried to get into shape before the trip, but even with all the work and therapy on my leg, I'm still limited from strenuous activities. Of course, some days, like today, the weather makes my leg feel stiff and slows me down even more. I sigh at the hill and start the slow climb.

In the end, the hill to the castle isn't nearly as bad as I imagined and Clara stays with me on the walk. It probably helps that there are a few other slower people on the tour: they make my slow walk seem less obvious. Since we're one of the first groups through the castle, we don't have to deal with a crowd. That helps speed up the tour.

Clara and I marvel as we walk through the castle, having never seen such opulence, and then fresh opulence because you can't have your castle looking outdated when the royal relatives come to visit. Over the years, I've met a lot of wealthy people and had the opportunity to visit and have dinners in some of the finest places across the country. I've never seen this type of wealth or intricate design.

When we come to the Royal Library, I decide it's my favorite room, with books lining the walls. They are primarily from the eighteenth, nineteenth, and twentieth centuries, we are told. I'm sure they're all first editions; the leather-bound books are kept immaculate. I can smell the leather, combined with a touch of something woodsy. The woodwork on the dark book shelves and furnishings are more detailed that I've even seen. I don't see a single flaw in the carved wood, just smooth lines. The library embodies well-educated, and worldly monarchs of an empire where the sun never sets. Even the Doll House's library matches the beauty and majesty of the Royal Library with its miniature books and furnishings.

Our tour of the castle is rushed near the end since we need to get to Stonehenge.

The ride from Windsor Castle to this stop isn't long, but the location seems so strange. It's practically next to the highway with nothing around it except the visitor center. As we approach the field with the ruins, I realize just how large and impressive the stones are, and like many before me, wonder how they got here.

I know there's a lot of talk about the possible spiritual connection that Stonehenge has. I wanted to think that would make me feel calm; instead, I find myself restless. I notice that I'm constantly checking the time and looking for our guide as I make my way around the stones with the audio guide. I lose Clara along the way and find myself rushing to get back to the meeting point. My reward is being the first person there and waiting for everyone else.

Our lunch stop is in Lacock, where I enjoy lunch with Clara, Linda, and Amanda. Linda and Amanda are the mother and daughter who just arrived from Ohio a few days ago. They are taking a few weeks to travel together before Amanda gets married this summer.

We spend most of lunch giving Clara tips for the next part of her trip because she'll be in the United States. The company and conversation are amazing: it's interesting to have four people from different places come together and agree on so much within hours of meeting. Being in the village of Lacock compensates somewhat for the touristy food that is served. The town is lined with picturesque English cottages, making me feel like I'm in a Jane Austin novel. We learned on the ride that the village was also the backdrop for several TV shows and movies. Unfortunately, the tour doesn't allow too much time in the village aside from lunch. As we take pictures around the town, I finally feel like I'm doing what I came to do—experience life.

When we arrive in Bath I realize that Lacock was just a pretty little excursion on the way to the real thing. Bath is amazing. It's a good example of European charm, down to the stones that we walk on. It feels like the whole town was designed to blend, a series of separate buildings harmoniously arranged. The architecture transports the visitor to a world hundreds of years ago. Once our guide distributes our tickets, we are sent on a tour of the baths with a meeting time for the bus back to London. Clara, Linda, Amanda, and I decide that although we want to see the baths, we also want to ensure we have enough time to have afternoon tea and walk around town.

The tour through the baths reminds me of the hot springs I visited in Colorado. Except that the history of the baths seems more mystical than scientific, more formal, and they don't have that strong rotten egg smell that the hot springs had. After the tour, we stop in a local shop just off the main square for afternoon tea to complete our day of British immersion. We spend the time discussing our travels and what we have planned for the following days.

As we stroll back to the meeting point for the trip back to London, we stop in a few shops. After spending so much on activities, I don't feel I have the luxury of buying souvenirs. Besides, I don't want to have to drag them around with me. The bus ride is quiet. Everyone seems tired after such a full day through the English countryside. As we pull into London

I make plans with Clara, Linda, and Amanda to meet for dinner the following evening.

The next morning, I make my way to the pick-up location for a studio tour of the Harry Potter movies. The pick-up location isn't far from the hotel, and the ride to the studio is only an hour. This morning the bus fills with mostly small groups, couples, and families with children. I end up sitting silently by myself listening to the commentary from the guide, which mostly contains information about how the tour works and a little tease of the studio.

Once we arrive, we are issued tickets and the group scatters, some heading straight to the entrance line, others stopping for pictures and then even more pictures. I suspect I'll never see some of these people until we board the bus at the end of the day. Once the tour starts with the cupboard under the stairs, everyone is on their own for the day. As I go through the studio, I find myself reading nearly every board of information and realize how differently I saw the series as a teenager reading the books and watching the films compared to as an adult recovering from a near deadly accident.

When I was in high school I was one of the popular kids. I didn't identify with the geeky main characters that are featured in the series and prominently displayed throughout the tour. The last time I reread the series, I connected with Harry more, the isolation that comes from being different from others. Even though people love you and try to empathize, they'll never understand exactly what you are feeling. There's no one to share the experience with—discus the strange looks or dismissal of your feelings. That's the overwhelming sense that settles on me as I go through the tour.

It's not all bad, though. The sets are magnificent, and I find with each step I'm learning something new. The tour is a glimpse behind the scenes, a chance to see how film works. Some people think it ruins the illusion to know how they make films, but for me it enhances the experience. I can know the tricks of green screen but still watch the movie and think it's real. All the detail that goes into each set, even if its barely used, is amazing. Every bottle carefully labeled, each prop with a purpose and a story of its own.

As wonderful as it is to finally have this experience, I struggle through the day. I shouldn't be struggling. Something is draining me, sucking the energy out of me. Having no one, other than a little plastic Eve doll to experience the studio with is one part of the problem. During my lunch stop I share some pictures on social media and chat with some people, but otherwise it's just me here thinking, *Oh wow, that's how they did that* instead of talking about that revelation with a companion. In the bathroom I catch a glimpse of my scar and stare for a minute as I follow the line of it down my face. After I've established that it's the same as it was yesterday, I go back to my tour.

I find myself making up stories about the people I see. Somehow all their stories are more interesting than my own. I see a family: husband, wife, and kids. I figure they skipped school and work for the day and are using the time to bond, to connect with each other over something they have all enjoyed together as a family. Maybe the parents loved the books when they were younger and they had their kids watch and read them too. Now they have something to share as a family.

I see a couple a little older than me, holding hands and kissing throughout the tour. They seem more interested in each other than the studio. I'm convinced they're a new couple, still honeymooning. Maybe they've skipped work to have an all-day date. While having lunch, I hear the guy tell the woman to be quiet when he answers his phone because it's his wife. He proceeds to complain into the phone about work. Maybe I need to work on my impressions.

I take part in some of the videos and photos you can participate in while here. My favorite is the chance to ride a broom through the film. I'm not sure if it's just because it's fun, or if it's because my sister will love it. Jessica always tried to tell me I was a witch and to leave on my broom. Now for a few minutes I can, at least in a video that I can send to her. It's the highlight of the day for me.

At the end of the tour, we are dropped into a massive store with anything you could want to buy. I timed my tour of the studio so that I wouldn't have too much time to spend here. I didn't want to be tempted to purchase anything. Instead I take a quick look around and head to the meeting place for the return to London. The ride back is filled with chatter about the studio, who liked what, who spent too much money in the store. I listen to the other conversations until I drift to sleep.

I meet with Clara, Linda, and Amanda for dinner at a distinctly English pub. As we share about our day I find myself jealous of Linda and Amanda. They have a buddy with them to help when they get lost, take pictures of each other, protect each other, and simply share their experiences. That's the image I have until Linda goes to the bathroom. Once Linda leaves, Amanda goes on a rant about how her mother won't stop shopping. She'll wander into any shop she sees. Meanwhile, Amanda will try to get them to their reservations on time; they almost missed their time-slot for the London Eye because of Linda. Amanda seems so frustrated, and they're still traveling together for another week. Well, I guess there is an upside to traveling by myself.

That night in my hotel room, I pack my bags so I can use my free time in the morning to continue to see the city before my train to Edinburgh. I try to capture the experience of London in my journal but find it difficult to find the words. When I think back to the girl who landed in London and was afraid to take the Tube, I know that there has been a change in me. But I'm not sure what it is.

Chapter 5

I've been at home with Mom and Dad for a week. It's blissfully wonderful to be out of the hospital and the rehab center. Although it was easier then, there was never a restful moment. Whether it was one of my roommates or someone down the hall, some patient was always wanting or needing something. A perfectly quiet night would be interrupted by messages over the PA system, followed by nurses and aides running around, constantly checking vital signs and giving medication.

At home, there is none of that chaos. It's Mom, Dad, and the occasional visitor. And to be honest, the occasional visitor has dwindled to Jessica, Eve, and a couple neighbors. It's leaving me with a lot of alone time. I used to enjoy my alone time because there wasn't much of it. I cherished it. Now it's the norm, and I'm craving the ability to interact with people.

When the phone rings and I don't recognize the phone number, I still answer it. It's often a telemarketer. I engage them in conversation about their product for ten minutes. It's mean because I have no intention of buying from this person, but it's just something to keep my mind busy and not think about being broken. This game wears off, and I'm stuck watching mindless television.

I try texting Eve, but there's no answer, nor a message from my sister, Jessica. I finally hear from one of the old interns at the law firm. She tells me she's busy and can't talk. I put the television on while I read my book. The television makes me feel like other people are around.

I fall asleep while reading and find a different television show is on when I awake. I haven't received any new texts. I scroll through social media, and there's nothing new there either. At least Mom will be home soon; we'll have lunch together and watch a movie. That's been our afternoon routine since I awoke from surgery. I seem to get more restless in the afternoon, and it helps minimize the urge to do stuff. The more time that passes, the worse my need to do something gets. On bad days, I find myself nervously bouncing my leg all afternoon, which probably isn't good for healing. At least tomorrow the physical therapist comes. She will keep me busy for an hour.

"Emily," Mom yells from the front door. I expected her home for lunch an hour ago.

"Hey, Mom, where have you been? I'm starving."

"Emily, I told you that I had errands to run and I left food for you. You could have eaten awhile ago." She seems exasperated, but I don't remember her saying anything like that.

"I didn't realize you would be this late. You know it's hard for me to get around the house on my own."

"I know it's hard, but you can do it. The doctor and the physical therapist said you need to be more active." There's an edge to her voice as she yells from the kitchen. She makes it sound like I'm lazy. It's hard to get up, and once I'm up I can't carry anything with the walker or cane. I hate moving around when I'm alone. What if I fall and no one will help me up again or call an ambulance for me? I can't risk getting injured and not being able to walk again. I just can't.

I mumble, "sorry. I'm trying to do a little more each day." I feel my eyes get watery.

It's not the first time someone has tried to use guilt to make me feel better, and like Mom, it's often to get me to do something normal for them. But I never used to make lunch for myself. I would buy it and eat at my desk while I worked. I am, however, trying to do things. I make sure I get dressed every day. I even put on makeup most of the time. The hardest part is the constant commentary from everyone, as if I'm supposed to be better already. None of the people who give me a hard time have ever had a broken bone or needed surgery. They think you should just keep pushing yourself, and since you don't have to go to work, you have plenty of time to do things to speed the healing. The reality is that there is only so much you can do, and so much you can do each day to improve.

One of the first days in rehab, I meet someone who hurt himself during recovery. He taught me that you can overdo physical therapy without realizing it. I cannot imagine going through all of this again. There's a greater despair awaiting a setback in recovery. It's beyond pain: it's isolating. It's like thinking that a man alone on an island should be able to swim to a better place but he doesn't have the strength to jump in the water.

I wake to a chilly drizzly morning in London and finish packing for my second new city, Edinburgh, Scotland. As much as I want to spend more time in London, it's too expensive. I chose Edinburgh because I spent so much time discussing a trip there with my ex-boyfriend, Dagobert. It seemed like a good idea when I picked it as a stop, before I realized it would remind me of Dagobert. Now it's too late to unplan it. It will cost too much to change my plane tickets and hotel reservations.

I remember getting off the plane in London, being afraid and questioning myself, my ability to do this and more importantly, to do it by myself. Less than a week later, I'm ready to take the Tube to the train and the train to Edinburgh. Granted, I took plenty of time to research the route and the best way to get around, while also checking the costs of my options. But now I feel confident in my ability to navigate the train system.

As I drag my bags back to the Tube station and then to the Kings Cross Station, I can feel my step quicken. I even find myself annoyed with the tourists making me meander with my bags on the sidewalk. Although London is still foreign to me in many ways, it was just starting to feel familiar. I have adjusted to the placement of the street signs and to look the other way before crossing the street. Converting the dollar to the pound is quick math to me now. Fortunately, some of these things will be the same in Edinburgh.

I arrive early at Kings Cross Station and meet a girl from Oklahoma while trying to take some selfies of myself in the station. Penny reminds me of a younger version of Eve. She graduated from college two years ago and is exploring the United Kingdom on a ten-day trip. It's her first trip to Europe; she doesn't count going with her parents as a kid since she didn't do much more than go where she was told. She learned some things on those trips, though, so she's not a rookie traveler like me. Penny helps me by making me grab lunch at the train station before boarding the train so that I'll be guaranteed something to eat.

We sit together on the relatively empty train and head north through the tunnels before finally emerging to a drier, foggier day. It's difficult to see Emirates Stadium through the fog, but Penny needs to get a picture for her soccer-obsessed brother. Not long after that the urban scenery turns into fields of lush green grass and rolling hills highlighting the journey.

As the scenery changes, our conversation shifts from soccer to traveling alone. Although I often did it for business, Penny had never traveled by herself until this past week in London. She found it liberating to be able to do whatever she wanted whenever she wanted. It sounds like she didn't feel as lonely as I sometimes do, and most of her activities were by herself–no tour busses for her. It makes me realize that I've been thinking about traveling by myself all wrong. Maybe I shouldn't overthink it; maybe I'll get used to it. When the conversation shifts to our plans in Edinburgh, I'm sad to find that Penny isn't staying in Edinburgh, but heading up to the highlands. We could have had fun doing a few things together; instead, I settle for a few suggestions and tips.

When we arrive in Edinburgh, we make our way out of the train station and part ways. I contemplate walking the hill to the Old Town or taking a cab. In the end, I struggle up the hill to the hotel where I will be staying, walking was a bad choice; I should have taken a cab. As if going up a big hill with a suitcase isn't difficult enough, I must walk over cobblestones and nearly twist my ankle. How I managed to step on those uneven stones and feel every muscle and tendon in my foot while keeping myself upright, I will never know. The last time I felt that many parts of my foot and ankle was the blaring pain after the accident. I didn't even feel this much of my foot in physical therapy. It's amazing that the muscles in the arch of my foot and the opposite side of the ankle complement each other to keep me upright. It takes all my mental restraint not to swear off walking for the rest of my stay. I'll just have to be extra careful walking over uneven ground.

My hotel is not as nice as the one in London, but it's cheaper and well-located. Well, except for climbing a gigantic hill. Now that I'm at the top, I'm okay. I want to call this an adventure, but no matter how hard I try, it's just been hard work.

The hotel is old but with a certain charm, but that might just be related to the older look of the building when I enter. Coming from the United States where anything built before the 1950s is old, I am getting a new appreciation for the definition of the word *old*. While checking in I get a few tips on things to do in Edinburgh. Since I don't want to spend Saturday night alone in my hotel room, I decide to do the suggested literary pub tour. I have enough time to unpack, freshen up, and take a slow walk to the meeting spot.

I window-shop along the way to the pub crawl and make mental notes about how foreign this city feels. I thought London was different, but this is yet another step from normal. The buildings are older, bordering on medieval; the streets are charming, crooked and uneven. And the hill that connects the old town to the new town is brutal, but I can't deny the scenery is majestic.

I grab a quick dinner along the way and arrive a few minutes early for the tour. While the group isn't large, it's large enough for me to hide in the background and become another random face. While the tour is fun and entertaining, it's also educational. I lose track of time as we go from pub to pub to learn some of the literary places in Edinburgh. While we don't walk far during the tour, I feel that I have a more intimate knowledge of the city already.

On my way back to the hotel, I stumble upon The Balmoral, the hotel Dagobert and I had planned to stay in when we came to Edinburgh. His mother always spoke so excitedly about her visit here years ago and how she just missed the Queen having tea at Palm Court. Seeing it is like a knife into the heart. It's a beautiful building and about as different from my hotel as it could be. Granted, both are beautiful old buildings, but the comparison ends there. The Balmoral is at least five stories with a magnificent clock tower in the center. It majestically towers over Princes Street as if it owns the city. Just looking at The Balmoral, I know it is the grandest hotel in the city.

When my eyes settle on the doorman in a kilt, I return to reality, the reality that I'm in Edinburgh. And that I'm standing on a corner late at night gawking at a hotel. It's a wonder no one has tried to steal my purse. With one last glance at the hotel, I start walking back up the hill to my hotel, which seems drabber and dirtier than I initially thought.

My body is exhausted from all I did during the day, walking with my bags in London, climbing the hill to the hotel and the stairs in and out of pubs. I try to read before bed but fall asleep three pages into my book. It's a long night of fitful sleep with weird dreams. Dreams of a softer bed that I'm sharing with someone else, tea in a fancy hotel, and finally walking the streets alone at night.

I wake with a jolt to honking outside my window. I linger in bed for a while. My body hoping to fall back asleep because it doesn't feel rested. However, my brain is awake and ready to start the day. Unfortunately, it's too early to do much except walk around.

Between the weather and all the cobblestones, I find walking more exhausting than it should be, leading me to wonder how people with disabilities get around the city. Everywhere I step I feel as if I could twist an ankle or trip and hurt myself. The damp and cloudy weather has certainly had an impact on my not-so-old injuries, keeping me sore and stiff. I like to think I'm ready for challenges, but it's hard on my body. I don't want to push too hard. I continue going out and doing things, pretending I'm like all the other tourists I see, but I feel myself moving slower and more cautiously with each step.

Later that morning I make my way to Edinburgh Castle. It's still glorious, obviously built to last and protect the city for centuries. The hill to get into the castle isn't as glorious. I'm not sure how I made it up. I wonder how the old rulers would have walked to the castle. I'm still a relatively healthy woman with access to modern health care. I know some of these people were in pain with no relief. Of course, they probably had servants and soldiers to run errands if needed. Maybe I should stop complaining about my leg.

As I walk through the castle, I'm enamored with the appearance of it, including the Great Hall. I'm once again struck by how impressive it all is. The walls are painted with rich colors and are decorated with swords in patterns like you would hang decorative candles. Compared to Windsor Castle, it's much more modest with the emphasis on the military protection of the city instead of the wealth of a monarchy. Although I appreciate the luxury of that wealth in Windsor, I have a much stronger tie to the fighting spirit I sense at Edinburgh Castle.

Inside St. Margaret's Chapel, I say a silent prayer. There is something about this small and basic chapel that moves me. Perhaps it's the simple but graceful design, or maybe it's the way it survived thousands of years as a place of refuge. There is something here that calls to me to stay longer and be present in the moment.

It's later in the day, while having lunch, that I receive a text message from Aunt Sloane.

Text from Aunt Sloane:
I haven't heard from you in a few days. How's it going?

Text to Aunt Sloane:
It's great! The weather is everything you'd imagine it to be in the UK—cloudy and wet. I'm starting to feel it in my bones, it's making me tired.

Text from Aunt Sloane:
Slow down, you don't have to see everything! It's a long road, pace yourself. And bring a raincoat EVERYWHERE.

Text to Aunt Sloane:
I figured out the raincoat fast. Pacing myself has never been my thing.

Text from Aunt Sloane:
Keep trying or you'll get burnt out, and probably run out of money too.

In the afternoon, I take Penny's advice and go on a literary walking tour. Our guide, Harry, enlivens the city with his stories. The tour is smaller than some of the others I have done, giving me a chance to chat with Harry. He's a grad student in Edinburgh trying to make some extra money. We have a great conversation about books and how books can influence your attitude.

After dinner, I decide to do a ghost tour. I swore I would not do one of these tours after all the horror movies Jessica made me watch. However, I saw signs about them all around the city and thought it might be a nice way to spend an evening, instead of alone in the hotel. When I arrive I realize I'm the only solo traveler on the tour. There is a group of cute guys my age, and when we do quick introductions on the tour, I find that it's a bachelor party. Judging by how they are dressed and their talk of visiting clubs after, it's obvious they will be looking for more than ghosts in Edinburgh tonight. My first fear is that one of them will try to pick me up, but then I remember my scar and doubt I have to worry about that happening.

As our guide leads us through the Old Town, he tells us stories of murders and suicides and how the victims haunt the city. At first I thought this would be cheesy, and it is, but we are also seeing a lot of little corners I hadn't noticed. Later in the tour we go into the Edinburgh underground, an area that used to have vendors and that served as a market in the city. It's empty now, except for the tour groups walking through. There's enough lighting to allow you to see the area and any hazards, but is dark enough that you would want to be careful.

While we're stopped and our guide is telling us a particularly dark story, I feel something on my neck and instinctively jump. When I look back I see a couple of the guys from the bachelor party laughing to each other. It takes a moment to understand what happened, and although I've realized at this point that they are drunk, I still feel embarrassed. I'm thankful for the dark lighting to hide the blush on my face. I'm glad the guys from the bachelor party are the first to leave the group when the tour ends. I hang back for a few minutes with the rest of the group to make sure I don't run into them on the way back to my hotel.

The following morning I'm up early to start my day at Holyrood Palace, which reminds me a little of Windsor Castle. I enjoy seeing how each time period is reflected in the rooms. It's inside the Mary Queen of Scots Chambers that I'm reminded of the TV show *The Tudors*. The layout and atmosphere of the chambers resemble the ones used by King Henry VIII in the show.

Outside, I tour Holyrood Abbey, or what's left of it. Just walls and the ruins of the pillars that once supported the roof. Although it seems small by today's church standards, enough of it is left to tell a story of a magnificent abbey for the monarchy. Behind is a lovely park with enough serenity to be a relaxing location for families picnicking on a nice day. There would be kids playing soccer and adults running through the park. I let my mind drift until it's time to find myself lunch.

Instead of a traditional lunch, I walk to The Balmoral in hopes of getting a reservation for high tea. As I walk past the doorman and go through the entrance, I am greeted on my right by the hotel staff. Once I explain why I'm here I'm directed toward Palm Court. The lobby is stunning. The modern striped carpet perfectly offsets the intricately designed ceiling with a large chandelier, which has probably been hanging since the hotel opened. The carpet is so soft that my feet bounce with each step. It's the best feeling my feet have had since I left home. At first glance, the integration of old world and modern design seems like an odd mix, but once I see the whole lobby, I see how well they complement each other. It blends the turn-of-the-century, old-world feel with the modern touches that The Balmoral guests expect.

Unfortunately, I'm unable to get a reservation for tea, which in hindsight is probably best for my wallet. I spend a few minutes enjoying the atmosphere and imagine what it would have been like if Dagobert and I had visited together. Walking hand in hand as guests, we would go to our suite previously used by someone famous. Dag would have splurged for me to have that privilege, and then gone home and bragged about all of that to his friends and family.

As I sit here, I notice the background music is more upbeat than I would expect: it's the Bee Gee's singing "Heartbreaker." My eyes jump to look at the speaker as though the Bee Gees were sending me a message. I leave the hotel frustrated and hungry. The more I think about the vacation that will never happen, my frustration turns to anger making me hangry.

I have lunch at Burger King, where to my horror, I find myself sitting next to some of the guys from the ghost tour the night before. I shift my hair to cover my face and try to hide, but one of them catches my eye and announces, "Hey, it's the girl from the tour last night."

"Hi," I respond with a fake smile while I wonder if the day can get any worse.

"I'm George. Are you here in Edinburgh by yourself?" He has a giant smile on his face and seems genuinely excited to talk to me.

"No, I'm here with a friend, but she's sick." They don't need to know I'm traveling alone.

"Wow, that stinks. I remembered you from last night. You remind me of my sister. You look exactly like her. I think it spooked my friend. He thought she was watching us all night."

What? I look like his sister? "Seriously? That's weird." I can't believe I look like some random guy's sister.

"Yeah, my friend used to date her and he's still a little afraid of her. He can be a git at times and was in trouble with her a lot. Anyway, toward the end of the tour, we were trying to keep him away from you. He was hammered, and we were afraid he would try to talk to you and freak you out." This story is so strange that I wonder if it's true, but George seems sincere, and he looks like the boy next door with his ginger hair, dimples, and freckles.

George continues with his story while tapping his friend on the arm. "I think my mate here had to pull John away from you at some point."

His friend looks over, and it's funny to see the moment when he realizes who I am and the embarrassed look on his face. "Oh, hey, not-Maggie, sorry about John last night. Umm, don't worry, he's not here. You're safe."

When I go to grab my last french fry, I realize I'm done with my food and can leave without being rude. "Umm, well, thanks, guys. That's weird that I'm Maggie's doppelganger and that I would see you not once, but twice. I'm glad we straightened that out." I motion with my hand in a circle between us, then pack my garbage. I practically run out of the Burger King wondering what happened last night.

The rest of my day is much less eventful, and that night when I'm packing my things, I think about my time in Edinburgh. I find myself wondering what Dagobert is doing, and then remind myself that it doesn't matter. He's not here. But I am, and apparently I have a double running around. Who would have guessed? As the night drags on and I climb into bed, I find the two events slowly slip from my thoughts, replaced by those of my next destination, Paris.

Chapter 6

It's quiet for once as I open my eyes. I slowly look around the room. Finally, I see Dagobert standing on my left. I haven't seen him since the accident, however long that has been. In my drugged haze, I've lost track of time, although I've been semi-awake for days.

"Hey, you're here," I croak through my tired voice.

"It's nice to see you awake. You gave your family a scare." There's something in his voice that isn't right–it's not the loving voice I recognize.

"Where have you been? Every time I ask for you, they tell me you're working. It's been days." I try to keep calm, but even I can hear the frustration and desperation in my voice.

"Sorry, Emily. I tried calling a few times but always missed you."

"Dag, you never left a message, and I didn't see any missed calls on my phone. What's going on?" I know he hasn't been calling. I can tell by the evasive answers everyone gives me when I ask for him. I might be tired, but I'm not dumb. I want answers.

"I've been really busy at work; they gave me the Mullin's case. As you know, there is a lot to do and a lot of technical details to understand. I've barely left the office except to sleep." There's more passion in his voice talking about this case than there was when he said he was glad to see me awake.

"They gave you my case?" Maybe it's the drugs, but I feel like I'm in an alternate universe. The Mullin's case was my baby, a technical case, and Dagobert doesn't have the expertise for it. How did this conversation go this direction so fast? I needed to see my boyfriend; instead lawyer Dagobert is here. Why?

"Umm, yea, they needed someone in a rush. I just finished something else, so I was free to take the case. They didn't know when you'd be back, so I offered." He brushes away some of his dark brown hairs—it's a nervous tick few people know about.

"What?" I almost yell. "I was in a car accident and almost died and you stole my case? That's what you've been doing instead of visiting me or calling me? And they let you?" I haven't been this awake since the accident, and I'm not sure if it's a good or bad. Even in my aggravation I hear some beeping in the background getting faster.

"I came here last weekend, but you were unconscious most of the time. Besides, your family was here, I knew you were fine. When Bruce and Mitch came to see you, we got to talking about the case. I could tell they were reassigning it so I offered. You would have done the same thing."

He's using his pompous lawyer voice with me, the one he uses when he's trying to reason with an irrational client. It's never worked on me before, and it's pissing me off now.

"Hold on a minute. My partners came to visit me, and you, my boyfriend, used the opportunity to steal my case. *That* is why you haven't come to visit me in almost a week? And you think I would do the same thing to you?" I squint my eyes at him and then squeeze them shut at the pain that radiates through my head. That's when a phone starts to ring.

Dagobert picks up his phone and obviously starts talking to one of the junior lawyers who helped me with my case, probably Vivian. The conversation is short and in a totally different tone than he had been using with me.

A more intimate tone, particularly when he ends the call with, "Bye, hun."

His eyes bulge when he realizes his mistake. "It's not what it sounds like. We've just been working together a lot, she's helping to catch me up."

I see the guilt on his face as he tries to brush away his hair again.

"You just called Vivian, 'hun' with your 'can't-wait-to-get-you-into-bed-tonight' voice. Please tell me exactly what she's been helping you with."

"She stopped by after the accident to see you. She was worried about you. Anyway, we've spent a lot of time together working on the case. I don't know what I would do without her." There's pride in his voice as he defends her.

"Just the case?" I feel my eyebrows raise as I say it; hopefully he takes the cue not to lie to me.

"Yea . . ." He pauses before finishing, "well, mostly. We've hit it off, we're enjoying working with each other. We've become friends. She's been really cool and she can cook too. I don't know when she has the time." He's nervously babbling.

She's cooking for him? "If she's cooking for you, does that mean you're dating her?"

He's startled, starts to speak, and then stops himself. Finally, he mumbles, "Just friends, we're not dating. Besides, aren't you and I dating?"

"No, we're in a long-term, committed relationship. But it seems that while I'm lying in a hospital bed, you're sleeping with your new friend. Is that accurate? Or do you have a better explanation?" Is this really the first conversation I'm having with my boyfriend after almost dying? The silence extends. The fight in me slowly abates and I feel the pain throughout my body. But this heart breaking is the worst.

I slowly start to cry. "So this is it, Dag? You're breaking up with me while I'm lying in a hospital bed broken in pieces?"

He looks sad for the first time during this whole conversation. "I should probably go." He pauses for a few seconds, turns on his heel, and walks out of the room, without a second glance or word.

I glance at my alarm clock playing "Defying Gravity" this morning. It seems fitting since Eve made me listen to it a million times after Dag broke up with me. "It's time to trust my instincts. It's time to leap." It fits well since I'm flying from Edinburgh to Paris this morning, taking another step out of my comfort zone. I'll have to rely on the few words of French I remember from high school. *Bonjour.* I'm not sure how far that will get me.

The flight to Charles de Gaulle is uneventful, and although the line for passport control is long, it moves quickly and doesn't take long to get into France. The airport itself has a terrible reputation for layout. Perhaps I took too many flights from LaGuardia Airport, but Charles de Gaulle isn't nearly as bad as I expected. Maybe it's my lucky day. I didn't have trouble finding the bus into the city either.

Although the bus takes almost an hour, it provides a great introduction to the city. The city is elegant, and I love how the architecture shifts as we go block by block, representing the different periods of time in French history. I'm instantly in love with all of it, including the gold decoration that permeates the city.

As we approach our stop at the Opera House, I play *The Phantom of the Opera* through my headphones. Due to my lack of familiarity and the evening rush-hour traffic, I hear most of the soundtrack before I am dropped off. From there, it's a ten-minute walk to my hotel where I again look like a tourist dragging my luggage. I grin when I arrive at the distinctly French hotel in the 8th Arrondissement and realize that the ten-minute walk has taken twenty minutes. I have a grin on my face when I say a silent thanks that I made it with all my stuff.

Once inside the hotel I'm enveloped by dark woods and red furnishings, and I feel embraced by Paris already. My room is equally welcoming. It has an unusual shape. One of the walls is cut at an angle, giving the impression that the room is one of a kind. I unpack a few things and prepare for my late reservation to visit the Eiffel Tower.

When I ask at the front desk how to get to the Eiffel Tower, I'm given a map and a set of directions. It doesn't seem like a long walk, so I leave in that direction on foot.

I'm wrong.

When I start to realize how far I am from the tower, I stop and buy something to eat and grab a taxi to get there. Judging by the number of people at the park who are eating, drinking, and taking in the view of the Eiffel Tower, I'm not the only one to have the idea of picnicking here. I use my time to eat and people watch until it's time to climb the Eiffel Tower.

As I approach, I see several long lines snaking around under the structure. The lines seem enormous, and I wonder how long it will take. Even with my ticket I have to wait in a line to take the elevator. It's a boring wait because no one around me speaks English. I can't eavesdrop because I don't understand what anyone is saying.

Once I reach the top of the Eiffel Tower, it's all worth it—the long walk, the lines, the taxi, and the cool wind that has my blonde hair swirling above Paris. Paris is gorgeous at night; the lights reminded me of a high-definition Lite-Brite version of the city. The way the lights etch out each street below my perch. The lights illuminate the Arc de Triomphe, the Seine River, and other things I hope I can identify before I leave Paris.

After I get my picture and have my moment with the view of Paris, I make my way down and then take a cab back to my hotel. As much as I loved the movie *Midnight in Paris*, I don't think F. Scott Fitzgerald is going to pick me up if I walk back to the hotel.

One of the gifts I received before leaving home was an all-in-one pass to see the major attractions in Paris. My three-day pass will dominate my plans for the first three full days in the city. That is what gets me up early the next morning so that I can book some activities, like a tour of the Opera House.

I'm excited; today will not be a repeat of London. My first stop is Notre Dame, where I take my time lighting a candle for those impacted by the recent terror attacks in Paris and absorb the atmosphere of the cathedral. I also make the decision to climb to the top of the tower for views of the city. It is not one of my best decisions.

The first fifty steps aren't too bad. Sure, I am tired, breathing heavy in the tight space and already slowing my steps, but I feel determined to do this. Around one hundred steps, when I find I'm not even one third of the way up, I give up. I'm wheezing, my legs are shaking, and I'm continuously letting people pass me so I can get a breath. I slowly make my way down the eighty-one steps. My body is shaking and my head is fuzzy by the time I reach the bottom. I'm thankful to be in the fresh air. I sit on the ground and pretend to be staring at the church. I'm disappointed that I didn't make it to the top, but it hurts too much and my leg was already sore this morning from all the walking last night.

I decide to take a taxi to Musée d'Orsay. The museum is highly recommended by friends saying, "not to be missed!" While digging into my day bag for my wallet, I find my little Eve doll with her red pants and black top. I give her a quick once-over and shove her back into the bottom of my bag. I forget her as I walk into the museum.

It's not long before I'm staring at *The Lion Hunt*, trying to figure it out, but barely making out the lion that I know is there. I must look confused, and I'm startled when someone taps me on the shoulder. With a deep baritone and a light French accent he says, "I'm not a fan either. Try Van Gogh's work on the second floor. They are my favorites."

The tall, dark-haired man offers to show me where to find it since the English map has left me a little lost. Along the way, he tells me the history of the museum, how it opened in the 1800's as a train station, but was quickly outdated and no longer usable. He continues, "the station was used for different things for many years, but had no real purpose. Eventually the government made it into a museum; now it's one of the most popular sites."

"It is a beautiful museum, and a work of art." I respond, hoping I sound more intelligent than I am. I'm sure I sounded like an idiot when I said I couldn't find the stairs.

"The building just needed someone to see her beauty and find a way to make her shine. People are often too quick to replace things these days, instead of taking the time to find the hidden beauty in them."

I sense he's not just talking about the d'Orsay but something more personal. I'm not sure I want to go there with a stranger. "They've done that, it's gorgeous here." My remark makes me smile.

"We've found Vincent van Gogh. I'll leave you here to look at the art. *Au revoir*." With a smile he walks away before I realize that I didn't get his name. Instead of a name, he left me the gift of a beautiful Van Gogh self-portrait with a crowd of people huddled around it.

Beautiful might not be the right word, but my French friend was right. The blue colors and the rhythmic brush strokes remind me of the ocean coming onto the shore. The calm waters flow onto a fiery Vincent with a scowl on his face and a sadness to his eyes. I remember from my college art history class that Van Gogh suffered from depression. I see it in his eyes in this painting. The painting reminds me that what we see on the surface does not always represent reality.

Later that day, I take the bus to the Arc de Triomphe and have lunch in a tourist trap near the Champs-Élysées and love being in the area. The bustling activity enlivens me. As I wander the avenue, I enjoy the amazing effort each shop takes to make theirs attractive. But the clever and colorful windows are enough to entertain me on my walk. I don't feel the need to do more than look.

My tour of the Opera House is equally exciting. The designers spared no expense or missed a detail. I'm not sure which I enjoy more—the history or the play it inspired. If I could stop and close my eyes, I think I could hear the phantom sing.

The following morning comes too quickly, but with equal excitement for the day. My first stop will be the Louvre, hopefully before the crowds have a chance to grow. Once through the long security line, I search for a map. Aside from a sign or two highlighting a major piece of art, the Sully, Denon, and Richelieu wings seem indistinguishable to the first-time visitor.

Of course, my first mission is to find the *Mona Lisa*. As I make my way through the Denon Wing, I look up and see the *Winged Victory* raised up on stone at the top of the stairs in the distance. She has a small crowd around her, even at the early hour of the day.

The sculpture is a headless woman's body with magnificent wings. She looks like she's walking into the wind as her clothing blows around her; the flowing garment presses against her body, showing her curves. The dress wraps around her legs and flaps in the wind. She has no arms, but her wings spreading open behind her tell us that she's ready to act. She has an easy, feminine look and a commanding stance that defines her as a leader. I linger longer than I intended because she grabs your attention and doesn't want to let go.

Eventually I pull away from her and continue my way to the *Mona Lisa*. On the walls I notice several crucifixion paintings, followed by a series of Madonna and Child paintings. There doesn't seem to be much to represent the time between his birth and death, just the innocence of a small boy adoring his mother and the violence of death.

While my brain is still working through this dynamic, my eye catches a different type of painting. An old man is holding a young child. I'm not sure what initially caught my attention, perhaps the bright-red clothing.

The old man has a wart on his forehead and his nose looks like the skin is permanently bubbled. I touch my face in reflex, then stop myself. The child he holds is perfect, a soft and innocent face framed in blond curls. There is no judgment in the child's eyes, eyes that have not yet been taught the definition of beauty. When I finally look at the plaque next to the painting. I see it's called *Portrait of an Old Man with a Young Boy* by Domenico Ghirlandaio.

By the time I reach the *Mona Lisa*, a crowd has already formed. I'm surprised how small she is for a piece of art that has garnered so much attention around the world. I gawk from the back of the group and take a picture of her, only to realize my picture shows more of a reflection of the crowd than of her.

The museum is beautiful, rivaled only by the palaces I visited in England. Large wide hallways lead to giant rooms lined with paintings and filled with sculptures and statues from centuries past. Each piece also tells a story of their artist. Some rejoicing, others judging, all trying to make their impact on the world.

After a dozen turns, walking through at least twenty rooms and possibly ending in a totally different wing of the museum, I find a painting that calls out a criticism of the greed in society. A man and a woman sit next to each other at a table. He is counting his money and jewels. She's distracted from her religious reading and focused on the money her husband is counting. Neither seems particularly happy. The harder I look, the more the man reminds me of Dagobert in twenty years. I shake my head, sigh, and make my way to the exit. Perhaps I should be grateful I didn't become half of the *Moneylender and His Wife*. It's time to see more of Paris.

The rest of the day is filled with Rodin, the Panthéon, the sewers, and eventually a cruise on the Seine. On the cruise, I can finally rest my feet and watch the city go by as I listen to the audio guide speak to me. It's evening by the time I make it to the Arc de Triomphe, where I plan to visit the top. Until I read the sign telling me there are almost three hundred steps. After yesterday's failed attempt at climbing Notre Dame, there is no way I'm doing this. I know my limits!

Instead, I stand on the island and watch the cars drive around in circles. I wince when I watch people narrowly avoid accidents. It's intimidating to watch the traffic pattern; we have so few traffic circles at home. Aside from this one being so chaotic, I've started to see the value in traffic circles while I've been away. They keep the cars flowing. I wonder if this experience will help me tackle the traffic circle at Jones Beach.

After spending my third full day in Paris at Versailles surrounded by some of the most ornately designed rooms and gardens, I'm exhausted. Even though my brain wants to do something the next day, my body refuses to get out of bed. It is the first time in nearly two weeks that I have stopped and rested. My body needs it. I decide to rest and use the time to read and connect with people at home. Even though I have been stealing a few minutes here and there to catch up, I am still behind on e-mails from home. It's amazing how many people barely interacted with me after the surgery, but now that I'm traveling, manage to find my e-mail address. I guess my adventures traveling the world are more interesting than rehabilitation. Oh, and don't forget to send a tip or two about London or Paris because they are planning a trip there soon. Ugh!

I finally leave my hotel for lunch. I choose an adorable little café with outdoor seating and some patio heaters and blankets to fight the chill that's still in the air. I've had many meals alone, and it's the first time I don't instantly grab my phone or my book to pass the time while I wait. Instead, I watch the people walking by.

As I sit and take it all in, I realize that Paris reminds me a lot of New York City. The combination of Parisians rushing from place to place, intermingled with the tourists trying to figure out where they are going. It makes for a fun game of guess who's who on the sidewalk. I mostly focus on the ones who look like locals because they tell the story of the city. I miss the adrenaline rush from New York, that feeling that you have something important to do.

On my last day, I explore a completely different arrondissement of Paris, the Marais. I'm curious about it after reading a murder mystery novel set here. It's also one of the few areas that is open on a Sunday. As I walk around, I feel I have traveled back in time. There are still a few cobblestoned streets, which are lined with ornate buildings, gardens, and courtyards, each with a story. Stories of the executions they saw, wars they witnessed, or threats of demolition, and finally their revival. The story continues today with a mix of Jews, gays, and lesbians among the grand hotels, art galleries, museums, and quirky shops. At first it seems like an unlikely grouping, but it somehow works.

I navigate through the winding streets and find the shops are as unique and unexpected as their history. I find myself touching items I likely wouldn't find in the chain stores. The items are extraordinary, from masquerade masks, feathered pens, handmade journals, leather bound books, stained glass lamps, and a mix of vintage clothing and new designer pieces.

In one of the jackets I look at, I find a grocery list on the back of a business card from the previous owner. As I review the list, I try to figure out what they were planning on cooking, but I only recognize a few items with my limited French.

At lunch, I stop at a small local café and talk to the waitress, Sophia, who has brown hair, chubby cheeks, and is old enough to be my mother. Sofia helps decipher the items on the grocery list, which includes *champagne ou crémant, crème de cassis, foie gras, petits toasts, gâteaux apéro, veau, pomme de terre, crème fraîche, champignons, salade, fromage,* and *gâteau.* Sophia suggests they were preparing for a dinner party and helps me pick a meal inspired by the list. During a quiet period, she tells me a bit of the history of the area, from the eyes of a lifelong resident.

Sophia's mother grew up in the area, during the time of the World War II. Although her mother never talked about it, she said it was obvious that her mother had memories of the Nazi occupation. Her family survived and stayed in the Marias in the same apartment that Sophia now lives in. First her mother, and now Sophia have watched the area rejuvenate in the years since the war.

Sophia remembers a simpler time when she was younger, before the area was so popular. Although she loves how much it has grown, she misses that simpler time when there were fewer people, the shops were for locals, and the community was stronger. But time changes. She still loves working and living in the Marais.

Later that night I take one last stroll around Paris and the Eiffel Tower before packing up to leave the next morning. I find the rumors of the rude French to be mostly wrong. Just like in any city, there are people in a rush to live. But when you catch people at the right time and place, they'll make Paris come alive.

Chapter 7

Stupid, stupid leg! They fixed you!

I vaguely hear the nurse above the pain in my leg, "Does this hur–"

"AHHHH, Yes, that freaking hurts!" I yell as I try to pull my leg away from her hands. It's a wasted effort. I can't move my leg. There's a beeping to my left, two short beeps followed by a long break, then beep, beep again. It's annoying the living shit out of me. Can't they turn the machine off? Just make it stop already!

"Tell me again how you fell."

"I don't really remember; my left leg just gave out and then I was on the floor." I've told the nurse this at least twice, and the EMTs a dozen times. Do they think I'm lying? Is this a test? They've asked me this more times than they've asked my name and date of birth, and I never thought that was possible.

The beeping on my left is now complimented by a beeping on my right, except this is a higher-pitched, steadier beep. It's too much noise. "Can you do anything about all this beeping? It's driving me crazy," I demand of the nurse as I point my arms in each direction.

"I'm sorry. That's your heart beat that we're monitoring."

"No, it's not. I've listened to my heart enough to know that is not my heartbeat," The nurse seems to ignore me, adding to my annoyance.

"Miss Taylor, when did you get out of rehab?"

She seems so sweet and innocent when she asks, it makes me want to shove her stethoscope up her butt. "Just over a week," I grit through my teeth in response, and not just because I'm in pain.

As Nurse Innocent continues to ask about my history, my medications, poking me to see if things hurt, I'm mildly relieved to discover that it's only my leg that hurts. She's quiet for a while, and it feels like hours in hospital time.

"Miss Taylor, other than a few scrapes and the pain in your leg, everything else looks fine. We're sending you to get an x-ray of your left leg. They will bring you down shortly. Do you have any questions?"

"Do you think my leg is broken?" I'm not entirely sure I want the answer, but I also know that she'll never tell me if it's broken, even if the bone is sticking out of my skin.

"I don't know. I think you would be in more pain if it were broken, but the pain could be masked by all the medications you're taking. We'll have to wait for the x-ray. I see transport coming down the hall. It shouldn't be long."

Oh good, not long in hospital time will be a few hours but it'll feel like a full day. Unless things are bad, then things happen in an instant.

I wake early in the morning to catch my train to Caen to see the sites near Normandy. The journey takes about two hours and is uneventful. I use the time on the train to do some research on what to visit and to coordinate my plans with my host for my apartment rental.

Once in Caen, I meet with the apartment owner, Camille, to get the keys. She greets me with a bag of pastries and kisses on each cheek. Thankfully, she speaks nearly fluent English and offers some suggestions about what to do and where to eat. She seems to know the area well and has obviously given this speech often. She's not just my landlord for the next few days: she treats me like a guest in her home.

One of her suggestions is to rent a car. That thought makes me nauseous. I'm not sure why; I drive around at home. Sure, I was a little nervous the first few times I drove after the accident, but I've gotten over that. I hoped not to do too much driving while I was away, but I figured at some point I would have to. In the end, I tell her that it's an expense I can't afford but will consider it.

Camille is persistent. "The tours are *trop cher*, and they just herd you around in a giant group. It's much better if you rent a car."

"Thank you, Camille, but I have everything mapped out for the week. I'll be fine. If I change my mind, I'll let you know," I say to appease her.

"If you change your mind, go to the rental place right down the block. Tell them I sent you and they will give you a good price." She points to the left as she says it, then pats my hand, as though she knows I will change my mind. Meanwhile, I wonder if she gets a kickback from them when she sends them customers?

The first place I want to visit is the World War II Museum, which is supposed to be great. As I walk through the streets of Caen I'm struck by how relatively new the city looks. After London, Edinburgh, and Paris, Caen looks like a youngster. It has a modern layout with wide avenues for the cars and few indications of how old the city might be. There are just a few older buildings sprinkled throughout the city. It all starts to make sense once I go through the museum. The damage to Caen was much worse than I realized; nearly the entire city had to be rebuilt after the war.

The museum brings a very real history to life for me, because it takes me from not only WWII, but through the Cold War as well. As Americans, we learn about the war in numbers, a few pictures, or a documentary in a history class. However, there is no substitute for walking down a street and seeing a picture of what the street, and every other street around it, looked like after the war. There was nothing here but rubble and homeless people. Not the homeless people who can't afford a home, but homeless because there were no homes. How do you start to rebuild an entire city?

It reminds me of when tornados ravage a town in the Midwest, except in this case the tornado lasted for years. It's remarkable to see how the city rebuilt, and with all that was lost, it still finds little ways to commemorate the past. As beautiful as it is, I'm not sure I would like to live in a place where every corner might hold a reminder of the past. It's bad enough I can't hide from my past pains. There is a reminder every time I look in a mirror. What I wouldn't give to be able to live without it for just one day or pretend nothing happened to me.

The time passes quickly as I go through the museum. It's only when hunger pangs drag me from an exhibit to eat that I realize how much time has passed. It only feels like minutes; I've spent hours in the museum. It's a beautiful afternoon as I stroll through the city. On my way to my apartment, I stop at Abbaye aux Hommes and William's Castle, where I enjoy the views at dusk, something I never did at home.

The next morning I'm up early to travel to Courseulles-sur-Mer by bus, which, by all accounts on the Internet, should be cheap and easy. Although I knew the bus ride would be long, it's longer than I imagined, and as much as I enjoy watching the view outside the window, it grows old halfway through the ride. I sadly find myself bored and annoyed by the tight winding roads along the way. Even the cute little houses aren't cute enough to distract me. I envision them as cold and drafty in the winter with outdated plumbing. And why are the roads so close to the buildings and fences? That doesn't seem like good planning. But once I arrive at the Juno Beach Center, the long bus ride is almost forgotten.

The center focuses on the often-overlooked Canadian contribution on D-Day. Through an exhibit designed for children, I learn what life was like for the residents of Normandy and Canada during the war. It's a sobering experience, even as an adult. Although relatively safe in Canada, there probably was a fear each day of what would happen next and a wait for word on battle casualties. The sacrifice to ensure the troops had what they needed. None of that is an experience that anyone I know remembers.

After the museum, I take a walk through the town and along the beach. I try to take a few minutes to imagine what it might have been like here during the war, but default back to movies like *Saving Private Ryan*. The town is pretty, and I enjoy its slow pace after having spent so much time in intense cities.

As I turn a corner, I run into a family of four trying to take a group selfie. Just as my dad would do, I offer to take the picture for them. When I go to hand the camera to the father, he asks about what I have seen so far. The family was at the British Sector at Sword Beach earlier in the day, which he explains is nice, but there wasn't much to do. When I explain I probably wouldn't go there since I was taking public transportation, he suggests I should rent a car.

When I balk at the idea, he responds with, "No really, we had considered different options, but had a friend tell us you either need to rent a car or take tours all around; the public transportation isn't well designed for tourists. My wife considered it, and when we compared costs, we decided on the rental car."

"But there are four of you, and one of me," I counter before I remember the hour-plus bus ride back to Caen.

"When we first started planning, we weren't bringing the kids, so it was just two of us. And the car rental was still cheaper. It helps that it's a slower time of year. Check it out if you have a chance; I think you'll see more that way." He shrugs and wishes me well.

I give the car rental idea some serious thought on the way back to Caen. This time I enjoy the scenery more as we drive through the villages, and I realize some of these houses might be hundreds of years old and have some interesting history. However, during the second half of the ride, when I am itching to get off the bus, the car rental starts to seem like a really good idea.

I stop in the car rental company Camille had suggested and rent a small car for the following three days. As Camille promised, they give me a good price, and although it is a bit more than I wanted to spend, it is much less than I expected and cheaper than the tours I considered.

As evening wears on, the clouds and winds increase and rain starts to loudly plop on the roof as I get ready for bed. It's a restless night of sleep as the wind howls around me and the rain pelts the ground and roof of the apartment. When I finally wake in the morning, I am relieved to see that the rain stopped.

Once dressed and ready, I get my rental car and head for Arromanches-les-Baines and Gold Beach. But my first stop is at Sword Beach to see where the invasion started with the paratrooper landings. I hope the visit will help me understand more as I learn about the British efforts. I scheduled an English tour of the D-Day museum so I'm hoping to hear some stories.

One of the things I quickly realize is that the landing by sea gets most of the coverage of our history, especially in films. But it was the paratroopers who started the invasion and struggled through the night. Reminds me a bit of the defense on a sports team—all guts, no glory—as they say. Perhaps I should have watched *The Longest Day* instead of *Saving Private Ryan* before my trip.

After the tour, I chat with a woman named Christine in the museum shop. She points me in the right direction to see the beaches and Mulberry Harbor. She's one of the best English speakers I've met in the area, and I take the opportunity to get some recommendations from her. She tells me where to find the best cookies and caramels in the region, complete with highlighted map. I'm glad I have the rental car so I can track them down.

I spend the afternoon seeing where they built an artificial harbor. The remnants lay on the beach and sometimes extend into the ocean. After over seventy years, some have become part of the eco system. Yet they still sit there as reminders of the battle that was once fought. When I close my eyes, I can hear the canons, guns, grenades, and cries for help. It's a grim feeling, but one that also speaks to the sacrifices made here.

The beach and the town are livelier; I wish I had stayed here for my visit. I enjoy how the town works a bit as an extension of the museum. The guns and machines of war are peppered throughout the town to honor the men who fought here and to teach a little history to a passerby.

After a few hours, I head toward Bayeux, a town that remained relatively intact during the invasion. Bayeux has the gothic architecture and charm I expected. As well as the ever-frustrating cobblestone streets on beautifully winding roads with local shops and restaurants. I'm sure it helps that I'm visiting during the off season. There's no rush of tourists on the sidewalks to spoil my image of a small sleepy coastal town.

When I return to my apartment, I'm drained. I find myself going through the motions of making myself dinner when a wave of emotion hits me. Unsure of how to deal with the feelings, I call the only person I can think of who might understand what I'm going through.

"Aunt Sloane." I surprise myself when it comes out as a sob into my phone and I start to cry.

"Emily? Are you okay?" she responds with a rush of concern.

"What am I doing here?" I blurt.

"At the moment, you're crying hysterically and freaking me out. What's going on?"

"I'm trying to figure out what I'm doing here. I feel like I'm just running around different places looking at churches and museums and getting nowhere." I stop crying a bit. I can hear my aunt sigh.

"Do you remember what you said to me a year ago when you mentioned the idea of this trip?"

"Something about how I didn't want to die knowing the only thing I ever did was be a fancy lawyer writing contracts for rich people so they can make more money." I try to take some deep breaths and pick up a toy on the table to keep my hands busy.

"Right, and I told you there's nothing wrong with being a fancy lawyer doing all that. Do you remember what you said after that?"

I mumble, "No," between sniffles.

"You said you wanted to live with no regrets. You just didn't know how or what that meant."

I nod my head and finally find my words. "I still do, but I feel like all I've been doing is running around different places, seeing different things, but I don't feel any different, and I still have no idea what I want or what I should be doing with my life."

She continues to talk me through my breakdown as my tears start to fall again. "Emily, it's not going to all come together in a few weeks. You had a lot happen to you in a short time; it will take a while to find out who you are again. You need to give yourself more time to absorb everything you're seeing and learning."

I'm crying again. "I've seen so much the last few days and weeks, but I feel like the same person I was when I got on the plane in New York. I thought I would feel better by now, or at least feel like I've found a direction."

"I suspect you have gotten a lot out of the last few weeks, you just don't see it yet. Maybe try journaling so you can track things better. I think you'll find you're changing more than you thought you were. What did you do today that brought on this mood?"

"I'm in Normandy, and I've been visiting all the D-Day sights. It's amazing what was accomplished here. I'm glad they didn't know how much luck helped them when they invaded or they might not have been so brave." The shift in the conversation is calming me down, along with my Eve doll as I fiddle with her in my hands.

"Ah, I see now. You're getting past your routine world. It's a good thing. It means you're growing."

"I don't like growing," I mumble like a spoiled brat.

"No one does. They just like the result after they've grown." When I don't respond, she changes the conversation. "Where are you going next?"

"I'm seeing the American sights tomorrow and then taking the train to Brussels on Friday and Amsterdam on Monday. I hope I survive until then. I did get a recommendation for a place with good cookies and caramels, but they're far away. I'm not sure if I'll make it there." I'm starting to think aloud.

"You ended up renting a car, didn't you," she continues. "Then, of course, you should seek out a treat. It will give you a chance to see some more of the area, not just a bunch of battlefields." She laughs a bit when she tells me to send some candy home.

When we finally end our call, I feel lighter and hope she won't call my mother and stress her out. I drop my Eve doll on the table and decide it's time for bed.

The next day I'm out early to see Omaha and Utah Beaches, where the American's landed during the invasion. I start at Omaha Beach.

I walk along the beachfront where thousands of soldiers landed over seventy years ago to an inferno seeking their deaths. Even after seeing what Steven Spielberg has portrayed, I cannot comprehend how such a calm and beautiful beach could have absorbed such an event.

As I stand here staring at the beach and the ocean washes up, I notice an older man with medals on his jacket doing the same thing. I'm curious if he fought here, but don't want to bother him if he did. When he looks in my direction, I decided to ask him. "Excuse me, sir, did you fight here?" I inquire.

My question startles him as he takes a minute to break from his thoughts, finally answering, "No, I fought in the Pacific. I have some friends who fought here. I wanted to visit once for them." He pauses for a moment but continues, "Hard to imagine, isn't it?"

"Yes, I've been here for a few days. I keep getting little bits and pieces of history. It's slowly sinking in. But I don't think I could ever imagine half the impact of the invasion."

After a moment, he says "even my memories betray me of my history. They play through my head like a movie. Pieces here and there that are so spectacular I wonder if they are real and if they are, how I survived it. War will do that to you—trick the memory."

"How do you mean?" I cock my head when I ask.

"Memories are funny things. I remember being places, my friends remember me being places. In some memories I can recall every feeling in my body as a battle happened around me, down to a twitch in the ear. Others faded quickly, and even after friends reminded me of things, I don't remember them. But I've always remembered the good times with my friends. The quiet times when we laughed at things that weren't funny, except in that moment with that group of people." He chuckles now as though he's thinking about one of those moments.

"Were you in the army?"

"Navy, stationed in Pearl Harbor, after the bombing. I missed it by a few weeks. It seems I'm a lucky guy. I was on the slowest sinking ship in the Pacific, gave us plenty of time to be rescued before drowning."

"How did that happen?" He has me curious now.

"An explosion on the ship, not too bad, but in the wrong place. What's your story?" he asks, as if to change the subject.

"I almost died in a car crash a year and a half ago," I say dispassionately, as though I'm talking about someone else.

"Is that how you got the scar on your cheek?"

"Yes, then my boyfriend dumped me. I needed a break, so I'm on a six-month trip around the world."

"Did he dump you after the accident or because you decided to go on a trip around the world?" He has a stern look on his face as he asks, making the skin crinkle around his eyes.

"After the accident, days after the accident." It surprisingly rolls off my tongue with no self-depreciating thoughts.

"That wasn't very nice. They don't make men today like they used to. What's your name?"

"I'm Emily, and you're right."

"Well, Emily, I'm Joe. You'll make a good wife one day. When you get home look me up, I'll find a nice young man for you," he says with a twinkle, and I have no doubt he *would* find me a husband if I asked him to.

"Thank you, Joe, I might just do that." I laugh.

"I better go before the missus thinks I'm trying to pick up a younger woman. She knows how easily I fall for a hero." There's a glimmer in his eye as he says it. "Mildred is the jealous type." He winks before turning to leave.

Did he just wink at me? How cute. And did he just call me a hero? I look around and see no one else in the area. Strange. The thought fades when I look up and see the American flag flapping in the wind above the tree line. In some ways, it's such a normal sight to see, until I remember I'm in France, and realize the flag is in the American cemetery.

My last D-Day stop is in Sainte-Mère-Église to see the town where one of the first drops of paratroopers landed, and which now houses the Airborne Museum. Once the town was a fiery blaze as many of the men fell from the sky to take the city. It was literally raining men. One man got stuck on a church steeple and played dead while watching the carnage happen around him. It's the stuff of movies. I can't imagine hanging there for two hours, watching your friends killed and captured and then trying to play dead to avoid your own capture and possible death. When you think of all the times life sucks, and then you think of that, those other times don't seem quite so bad.

After all this morose thought of life and death, I decide it's time for a treat and follow the map to get some cookies and caramels. While the caramels aren't far away, the cookies take me into the country a bit more. The countryside is sprinkled with cute houses and farms on tight winding roads that were obviously designed before cars. It's quite picturesque as I drive along popping caramels in my mouth.

The cookies are a bit more difficult to get because no one in the shop speaks much English. We manage to communicate through charades.

That night the wind rises again while I pack. I remember Joe calling me a hero. I can't imagine why he would think that. I'm the girl who ran away from life when things got bad. He's the one who ran into death and was lucky to make it back home.

Chapter 8

" Dag, I still can't believe you got us a reservation at Per Se," I whisper so the other diners won't hear.

"I wanted to surprise you with something special for our anniversary, a delicious dinner and a beautiful view for my beautiful girl." He looks so proud of himself as he says it.

As excited as I am, I'm a bit concerned about how much this dinner will cost. But he doesn't care. He likes his fancy dinners and hates when I tell him I would have settled for pizza on the couch. I bet he's happy to see me so excited about this dinner. That makes me happy too.

The food is amazing and melts with each bite. It's a wonder I'm able to hold a conversation. We keep the talk about work to a minimum since it's our anniversary. I'm glad to have a night off from work and all that comes with it. I've been working insane hours lately with a big client that will make a difference to a lot of little people. Not that I don't love what I do, but I want tonight to be about Dagobert and me.

"Have you given any more thought to moving in with me? I think that's the next step, isn't it?"

I think he stuffed me with food to make me amenable before asking. He knows I want to move in with him, but that my parents won't approve unless there are signs of a marriage coming, primarily in the form of a diamond on my left hand.

"You know I want to move in with you, and you know what my parents will say. They love you, but they have more traditional ideas." He's still smiling, so that's good.

"I know, and when is your lease up?"

"In the fall, end of October. Don't play dumb with me. I know you know the exact date." He has a goofy grin on his face, and his eye has a subtle twitch to it, the type you only notice when you spend a lot of time with him. He's up to something.

"Hmm, perhaps we should do some ring shopping soon, get some ideas of what you might like." His goofy grin has spread to a giant grin that fills his face with joy.

"Do we have time now?" I'm pretty sure my face matches his.

He laughs, "not tonight, but soon. Maybe tomorrow? The shop is near work, if I can ever drag you away from the office, we could go at lunch or after work. Maybe one day this week?"

He sounds eager, which is amazing. He usually skirts my questions when I ask about getting married. I guess I should keep the baby talk to myself, tonight at least. After being together for three years, he's finally showing signs of being ready to commit. I was afraid this moment would never come.

When the check comes, he quickly takes it from our waiter, yet there is a moment when he's getting his credit card out that I can sneak a peek at the cost of our dinner. Oh my, I've never spent that much on dinner for two! Dinner was good, possibly the best meal I've ever had, but I'm not sure it was that good. The night isn't over either. We still have tickets to the opera.

After the emotional visit to Normandy, I weekend in Brussels on the way to Amsterdam. The weekend mostly involves beer, chocolate, and seeing a statue of a boy peeing. I also stayed in a hostel, which wasn't nearly as bad as I expected.

After staying in hotels and even the rental apartment, I was nervous about staying in a hostel, but a friend suggested one she stayed in once in Brussels and said it was nice. I figured it would be a good test for a shorter part of the trip, and I was able to book my own room so that I had at least some privacy. When I found the hostel, I discovered I could stay in the heart of the city, and the price was amazing compared to hotels in the area.

The hostel is old, but clean and has a lively vibe. There's a nice hustle and bustle to the lobby area with young people coming and going and a lot of community space. As I go to use the bathroom, which is separate from my room, I have the realization that for the weekend I will never have my own bathroom. I don't know why this never occurred to me, but the lack of privacy suddenly does. Will I be on display this whole part of the trip? I try to remind myself that no one else cares what I look like, that no one will notice I have a limp or will see my scarred body. I'm only partially convinced.

With my lower-end accommodations, I find myself out exploring the city more than I probably would have if I were staying in a hotel. It allows me time to soak in the European flare of the city and visit a variety of churches and museums.

Amsterdam is my true destination. While known for being a bit of a party town, it's also known for beautiful canals, bikes, clogs, and cheese. I am also happy to find that English is widely spoken. While I haven't run into any real trouble with languages, there were a few occasions where there was some initial confusion and frustration.

I find myself staying in a hostel in Amsterdam as well, and I enjoy the frugal mentality of the guests and staff. When I checked in, I asked for some recommendations for things to do that would good and cheap. I am rewarded with an entire list of activities and an explanation about how the bike lanes work so that I don't get in an accident.

The Australian girl who checks me in points me in the right direction to walk and get my bearings before dark. Staying near the Red Light District, I quickly get a peek of what Amsterdam has to offer, from coffee shops, which didn't serve coffee, to sex shops, and places to lose yourself in fabricated seduction. I'm curious about the rumors, particularly because it doesn't seem as seedy as I expected.

When I sit down to dinner, I go through the suggestions they gave me at the hostel. I decide on some free and discounted tours that I can book at the hostel. By the end of dinner, I'm relieved to have a rough plan for my days here.

The number one thing I want to do in Amsterdam is visit the Anne Frank House. After dinner, I book the earliest admission ticket for the morning. I prepare for the day quietly so I don't wake my roommate. When I arrive, the line is already down the block, but I somehow only end up waiting a few minutes for entry. Like most girls my age, I fell in love with Anne Frank when we read her diary in school. If I think back, it's also around the time my interest in World War II started. Although the story is a fading memory, the emotions settled back once I stepped into the museum.

The museum has a slightly different set up today compared to Anne's time, but it still does an excellent job of showing what it looked like when Anne was hiding. As a busy woman, who, even after nearly dying, still can't quite slow down, I cannot fathom living in such conditions. The area the family had to live is slightly bigger than the size of my apartment in New York City. They had to talk softly, move quietly, and were stuck with the same small group of people for years. I could barely stand being at work all day with the same group of people or living with my parents after living on my own for so long. I suppose self-preservation plays a huge part in it, but I still can't imagine my life like that for even a day.

As a child I always wanted to believe I would have been like Miep Gies and hid my friends from the Nazis and saved a young woman's diary. Well, maybe before the accident, I would have done that. Now I feel more like I'm floating through life, just surviving, unable to help rescue someone else—or their diary. I'm not even sure I would make it up all the stairs. The place is like an obstacle course. I would have been caught and shot.

I climb all the stairs. I figure if Anne could live like this for over two years, I could try it once. After a few more minutes observing all I can, I crawl back out with little grace and am thankful for life.

I have a lot to consider as I walk through the canals in the shady light. The city is different during the day, quieter than the night before. The people headed to work are already there. That leaves me surrounded by tourists, mothers with baby carriages, and little old ladies headed in the same direction as I am for an afternoon concert.

I line up early to get a good spot at the opera house for a free performance. It's one of the things I've missed in the past year and a half. I used to go to shows and performances regularly in New York. Enjoying the free show, I drift back for a half hour to that period in my life. It's a half hour of which I can pretend I have no worries and a bright future. My body sways to the music. I leave the theater with a smile and head to the meeting place for an afternoon walking tour.

For three hours that afternoon I am guided through the streets of Amsterdam by a dark haired and blue eyed Hans, learning about government, canals, dams, World War II, the Red-Light District while being reminded about the city bike lanes. That is a quick lesson when someone from the group almost gets run over by a bike within five minutes of starting the tour. Hans brings the city to life, and I know I will appreciate the city more because of it. At the end of the tour, I ask Hans a few questions, and he somehow talks me into taking another of his walking tours in two days. He tempts me with the lowest price he can offer me. Perhaps I tipped him too much at the end of the tour and he wants me back to do it again.

Exhausted, I decide to rest a bit in the hostel before I go to a free jazz show that Hans suggested that's happening at the Bimhuis, a well-known jazz club. My roommate, Helen, invites herself along to see the show. The city doesn't feel unsafe at night, but I'm glad to have a buddy. Although Helen and I are quite different—she is Australian and fresh out of college on a gap year—we make a good pair for the night, watching out for each other and giggling as we walk back to the hostel.

The following morning we both sleep in. I manage to get myself out the door in time for another free concert and to explore the Van Gogh Museum. After an hour or so of walking around the museum, I conclude that although he was a very gifted artist, he was gloomy at times. After I realize I've been staring at the same painting for several minutes, I break from my spell and overhear a guide talking about Van Gogh's self–portraits and learn something new.

Van Gogh's use of such a serious face in his paintings isn't related to his depression; it was a common style at the time. Apparently he was working on different colors and techniques, and he provided himself with a cheap model. That would explain why the self-portraits are all so different in look, color, and style. I should have paid more attention in my art history class.

The days after are filled with street markets, picnics, and my second walking tour with Hans, Alternative Amsterdam. Although it does cover some of the same things as the initial tour, it goes into more depth on some things and is a reminder that not everything is as it seems. The legalization of prostitution, the good and the bad of it. The same with the legalization of marijuana, regulations allowing a certain level of control and, of course, the people the drug attracts. I suppose it's no different from social issues we have at home. When I first met Hans, I thought he was cute and smart. No wonder it was so easy for him to sell me on another tour with him. As interesting as Hans is, and as much fun as I had on his two tours, when he asks me to go for coffee after the tour, I decline. I think his version of coffee and mine are different. Besides, he's too free spirited for me.

A few days into my stay, I finally get to take a tour I'm super excited about, a countryside bike ride, bad leg and all. We meet in the late morning and start riding through the city. It's fun to be the crazy one in the bike lane ringing my bell at unsuspecting tourists. I even mount my little Eve doll so she can enjoy the ride with me. Although the weather is still cool, it's a nice morning and the breeze feels refreshing with the sun on us during the ride. However, it doesn't take long to start feeling tired. It's just after getting out of the city that I start to realize that all the walking I have been doing has not prepared my body for a bike ride. My leg muscles start to burn and my breathing quickens as I try to catch my breath.

It's fortunate that our guide keeps a relatively slow pace with frequent stops. It makes it less obvious that I'm the slow person in the group. But I know it, and I'm sure others notice. I'm constantly bringing up the rear and one of the last ones to stop at each break. There's one other girl in the group who seems to be struggling, but she obviously has a hangover. I'm not sure if that makes her more annoying or more sympathetic to everyone else. Maybe everyone in the group has suffered a hangover in the past, and understand it. But are they wondering who books a bike tour when they're in terrible shape? I know I am.

Finally, we make it to our farm stop for our forced cheese-and-clog demonstration. I'm sure it's a ploy to get us to buy stuff. I'm just happy for the break. The cheese demonstration part is interesting, for me at least. The girl who is hungover doesn't seem to appreciate the smell and leaves shortly after it starts. I enjoy the tour and the tasting of the farm-made Boerenkaas. I might even try to use my newfound knowledge when I go to the next market.

The clog demonstration, which I was skeptical about, isn't bad. Our cute male presenter, Nick, has adorable dimples and is entertaining, which helps. I give this brown-haired man credit for synthesizing eight hundred years of clog history and making it fun. He even makes me wonder if I should buy my mother some clogs for gardening at home. I dismiss the idea when Nick tells us about the tradition of making clogs as part of a marriage proposal. Back in the day, the man would make special clogs for the girl they liked and leave them outside the house for the girl to find. If she wore the clogs, that was her way of saying yes. While I can appreciate the practicality of this tradition, it seems lame. There's no fancy proposal over a nice dinner, or even a hotdog at a baseball game. You don't need a manicure to clean up your hands and show off your new diamond ring. They're clogs; good for walking in the mud. Despite the bad things I could say about Dagobert, at least I know he wouldn't have gotten clogs to ask me to marry him. During one of the breaks I decide to text Eve so she can laugh along with me.

Text to Eve:
Men used to make fancy clogs here for engagements. Can you picture Dag making me clogs?

Text from Eve:
You've got to be kidding me? Do you think he even knows what clogs are?

The rest of the ride back to Amsterdam is a struggle as my leg and ankle are sore. It's a miracle I don't fall on the sidewalk and collapse when we're done. Instead, I hobble away from the tour and find myself reading in bed later in the day.

Helen drags me out of my bed at night for drinks, and I only go because it's her last night in the city.

It's pouring rain on my last day in Amsterdam. I have a lazy morning before going to visit a few sites. As I dart between the raindrops, I'm glad the rain keeps some of the bikes off the road. I feel safer without them. Perhaps it's a sign that I'm ready to move on to Berlin.

Chapter 9

W ho talked me into this? Eve, of course. We used to go clubbing all the time. As time passed and our lives changed to include boyfriends and living in separate cities, we didn't get to do it as much. Before the accident, it had been months since we had gone clubbing. But here I am, months later and still healing, being dragged out to a club.

I tried everything to get out of going out. I'm sure there's a good movie on Netflix I could be watching. Instead, I'm wearing my oh-so-sexy boot from the doctor with a short, skimpy, and sparkly red dress that I used to love. Right now it seems like the stupidest dress I ever bought. I used to enjoy dressing up for Dag. It would bring out a little bit of the alpha male in him when we went out. I liked knowing he was keeping an eye out for me and my friends to make sure no one took advantage of us. Now I feel like this dress brings everyone's attention to me, include the men Dagobert tried to protect me from. As an extra bonus, the way I walk with my sexy boot makes my dress creep up my legs faster too. I'm constantly tugging it back down.

"Stop fidgeting, your dress is fine," Eve sighs as she yells at me again.

"It keeps riding up. I feel like a tramp." I give Eve a side eye.

I haven't really needed to wear my boot much these days, but I find it helps when I'm in unfamiliar environments. It also helps keep people away a bit, giving me a little more space. In the club, though, there isn't much space to be had. The dance floor is packed; the bar is packed; there are no seats anywhere. We end up standing to the side, and Eve goes to get us drinks while I hold up the wall. It's a sturdy wall. I think it holds me up better than I hold it up.

As we stand there drinking, Eve tries to point out cute guys to dance with. I reject them all, but eventually send her off to go dancing with one who comes up to us. A song or two goes by before she comes back for me and drags me onto the dance floor. *Drag* might be a strong word. Navigating through the people is a challenge, and I step on a couple feet along the way. I last about a song as I try to wiggle my body on the dance floor in a way that resembles more Monica from *Friends* than Beyoncé on stage. I feel exceptionally awkward and notice some people staring at me and my foot. I'm feeling very exposed, and after another song, head back to the wall that needs holding up.

It takes ten minutes to go about ten feet because I try not to step on anymore toes along the way. The people are densely packed so I'm jostled as I shuffle. I don't feel like I have solid footing as I move along and am relieved to reach my old spot. Eve continues to dance for a few more songs before coming back to me. "I tried, I really did. Can we just go home?" I plead with her.

"Okay. I'm not sure you tried that hard, but I'm glad I finally got you out of the house on a Saturday night to do something other than watch a movie," she responds with a sigh and turns to leave.

After she turns, I roll my eyes at her comment knowing that I did try. Easy for her to say when she walks normally and doesn't have a giant scar on her face advertising she's a freak. Going against the flow of people is even harder as

I hang on tightly to her hand so that we're not separated, but eventually we make it to the door and head home before midnight.

On my last morning I try to quietly finish my packing so I don't wake my roommates and then head to the train station for the train to Berlin. It's a long journey to Berlin so I make sure to arrive early and find myself a window seat and can watch the landscape as we cross borders. Shortly after the train departs, my seatmate asks all the simple requisite travel questions: Where are you from, where are you going, how long are you traveling? John is a Canadian in Europe on business for a few weeks. The conversation quickly turns to some of our favorite and least favorite things we've seen while traveling.

"Edinburgh seemed like a great city, but I think it had too many bad memories attached to it. I never connected with it the way I did other cities," I explain to John.

"I've come to Europe once or twice a year for the last three years, and the most interesting thing is that each time I come my opinion changes. My first time I loved Berlin and hated Amsterdam. The second time it was the opposite." John pauses for a moment as though processing his own comment. "Now I've grown to love them both for their own personalities. When I look back, though, I had different things going on in life. Now that I know my way around, I feel more comfortable in the cities. I feel less swayed by my mood. You know, instead of being in a bad mood and hating Berlin, it becomes I'm in a bad mood and I'm in Berlin. Does that make sense?"

"It does. It will be interesting to see how I react to some of the places that I don't know much about, like South Africa. Then compare my reaction to places that I think I know a lot about, like Italy." My mind starts to really work as I realize how little I know about South Africa, except that there was really bad crime there in the 80's, or was it the 90's? I hope what everyone is telling me is true and crime is significantly lower now.

The conversation eventually dies. I read my book and fill out my journal for the rest of the ride to Berlin. We arrive in the afternoon, it's a short trip to my hostel this time. When I walk through the door I know it's the nicest one I've stayed in. The first thing I do after dropping my stuff off is get a few suggestions for a rough itinerary, which I work through while I eat dinner.

The following morning I start my day in Alexanderplatz with a walking tour. The city is already alive with people rushing around to work or running errands. The shops are just starting to open when I arrive, and as I look around I notice the architecture in this area is a bit depressing. All boring lines filled with cement.

Our guide starts the tour at the Marx-Engels Forum with some background on the origins of Communism and then moves into the history of the city before World War II. Most of the tour is centered on WWII and the Cold War.

The citizens of the city were terrorized through much of this history, starting with events like Kristallnacht and the deportation and killing of the Jews. If that wasn't enough, angry Russians, bitter over how they were treated on the eastern front, were ready to mercilessly revenge themselves on German citizens. The last bits of dignity were taken from the citizens, their homes seized or destroyed; the little food left was stolen or simply destroyed out of spite. It feels like a history generations old that you learn about in school because there is no one alive who remembers it, but it's much more recent than that.

After the war, Berlin was cut into pieces by the Allies. East and West Berlin were divided up and eventually separated with a wall. It reminds me of the dystopian books I've read over the years. Those stories are never so real as when you see a piece of the history that inspired them. It's prevalent everywhere you go in the city. From the markers showing where the wall once stood, to the book-burning memorial in Bebelplatz, to the oppression as you wander through the Topography of Terror.

The tour helps me absorb the history of the city. It highlights the differences that exist as I freely cross from East to West Berlin, and see the architecture, shops, restaurants and even feel the vibe of the city. While it's obvious the city has blended together, there are some scars from that time that will likely never go away.

During our tour, we are taken to Nordbahnhof, the ghost station exhibition for the train stations abandoned in 1961 due to their location in East Berlin. The closest thing I can think of when imagining riding through an empty train station each day is my father talking about how abandoned Lower Manhattan was after September 11. He had to be escorted to his office to pick up materials and documents for his company, and when they moved back into their building, they were one of the only companies for a while. He remembers the eerie and unusual quiet for a once busy and lively area.

On a rainy day in Berlin, I visit the Checkpoint Charlie Museum where the checkpoint from east to west operated during that time. The museum details post-World War II Berlin and the Cold War and, of course, those people who tried to escape East Berlin for West Berlin. Communism wasn't popular with young Germans; many just left East Berlin. The Russians weren't happy, and one night people went to bed semi-free to move around the city and awoke to a physical barrier separating the two halves of the city. Followed by a fence and eventually growing to the Berlin Wall.

I wander through the gift shop and notice a replica of a drawing that visually tells the story of East and West Berlin. The sun shines on one half of the scene; it is lush and green with flowers growing. Near the edge there is a tree with fruit hanging and a bird signing. A girl sits below watching the happy scene in front of her, a boy and girl playing catch. In another area, a woman is walking a dog and pushing a baby carriage. Everyone is happy and enjoying life on one side of the image. In the middle of the page is a wall lined with colorful flowers, but separates this happy scene from the other half of the picture.

The opposite side of the wall is lined with barbed wire. The sky is dark and stormy with bolts of lightning flashing down from the clouds. The ground is a stark gray and white, and there's a tree in this section too; however, it's dead, as is the bird sitting in it. The people are all either walking skeletons or bodies with missing limbs. The color in this section of the picture doesn't come from green grass: it comes from the puddles of blood intermixed with the skeletons and broken bodies. Instead of flowers, the ground is littered with explosives and containers decorated with skulls and crossed bones.

Before this moment, nothing prepared me to understand why people would risk their lives to leave East Berlin. This picture did. And although it's just one depiction, it tells the mind-set of a people. The mind-set where nothing is possible, where you live until you die, likely a painful death.

I'm in a somber mood after visiting the museum gift shop and decide to head back to the hostel and absorb what the day has taught me, then try to relax. While reading, a new roommate enters the room. Amber is from the Washington, D.C. area and will be in the room through the weekend. It's nice to know that there will be one less bed all weekend with a rotation of people.

She didn't hang around long after she arrived, but we have plenty of time to get to know each other when we are both getting ready the following morning.

"Where are you going?" I ask when we are leaving the room.

"Day tour to Dresden. You?" she responds as she slings her backpack over her shoulder.

"Same thing, nice coincidence. Is your name Jen?"

"No, it's Amber." She doesn't seem terribly fazed by my mistake.

"Wow, I wasn't even close." I groan to myself for being so rude but try to laugh.

"I think you're thinking of the other girl in the room. Her name is Jen."

"Right, well, at least I know where I got the name Jen from." I feel a little less stupid.

We spend the bulk of the day together, and I find out that Amber is twenty-seven and taking a two-week trip through Germany for a vacation. She invites me to do a pub tour the following night with her and Jen, which I happily agree to do. I wanted to do a pub tour, but didn't want to go alone. This is the perfect solution. It's nice to have someone you know to keep an eye on you when you're out drinking. And after a day with Amber, I feel comfortable with her and know we'll watch out for each other.

The following night Amber, Jen, and I dress ourselves up as best we can with the clothes we have for traveling. I have a nice top appropriate for the night, and Jen forces me to wear an extra skirt she has. It's skimpy and black. Not exactly my style these days, but it feels good to be dressed up again. I make sure to take a selfie with my little Eve doll and send it to Eve before we go out. If anyone will appreciate my being dressed up and going out, Eve will. She makes me laugh with her response: "Love it! Have fun and find some hot guys."

We meet the group at 9:30. There's at least twenty-five of us so it should be a good time. The first bar isn't too far away, and Sia is singing in the background when we start talking to Josh and Brad from Los Angeles. It doesn't take long to figure out they are a couple, and adorable. They finish each other's sentences and give each other shy smiles throughout the course of the night. They get cuter the more they drink.

At the second bar, we find ourselves playing drinking games with Fifth Harmony singing in the background. Not that you can hear much of the music because our group is in such a good mood with everyone yelling and cheering through the game. Although none of the penalties force anyone to drink much, everyone half moans, half cheers whenever they lose.

Our third bar is unexpected. It's a hookah bar. Josh explains that it's a water pipe with tobacco and not marijuana, as I first thought. Although I'm not interested in trying a hookah, I eventually take a puff, just to say I did it. Although I don't particularly enjoy it, I can see how someone might like the experience. Everyone seems more relaxed after a few minutes. The bar has softer music, giving Josh the opportunity to try and talk me into going to India.

"You *have* to go. It's the most amazing place ever and it's where I met Brad," Josh pleads with me, even getting down on his knees for effect.

"I already have most of the trip planned out, and I didn't plan on India," I inform Josh. The truth is that it seemed too different to me, a chaos that would just add to the chaos inside my head. It would be too much

"Skip Italy. You can get good Italian food in New York City, and the history in Italy has been there for centuries; you've got time to see it. But India will change your life. The people, the place, it'll rock your world. Right, Brad?" Brad's not paying attention. He's deep in conversation with Jen about the different flavors for the hookah. Apparently apple is the best.

"Maybe on another trip. I'm not ready to rock my world that much. I'm trying to rock the boat, not tip the boat over. Been there, done that, I didn't bother buying the T-shirt." Fortunately, I'm saved when our guide announces it's time to leave the bar for our last stop, a big club, and it should be hopping by the time we arrive.

As we enter the club, Kesha is playing in the background and the girls drag me onto the dance floor while Josh and Brad get us drinks. On the dance floor, I hear my heart beat to the sound of the drum. My body moves to the music as the lights flicker in different colors to the rhythm of the music. Josh and Brad show up with our drinks. A song or two later and we all dance as a group as the music keeps pumping.

It's not long before a guy starts dancing with me. It brings me back to my old days of clubbing with Eve and occasionally with Dag. The fun of two bodies together on the dance floor feeling the music. Until the strange guy gets a little touchy-feely with me. I push his hands away from my hips a few times, but he doesn't take the hint. Thankfully, Josh does. He quickly jumps in and steals me as a dance partner. Mr. Touchy-Feely looks annoyed and leaves. I see him later dancing with some other girl, his hands all over her body. She looks happy as they dance to "I Kissed a Girl."

I'm just starting to tire when I get bumped by something hard. I look behind me and there is a girl on scooter-type thing. She quickly apologizes, or at least I think she does. I can't hear much of what anyone says. But I keep looking at her longer than I should and realize she's dancing her heart out on her little scooter with a boot on her foot. It's the craziest thing I've ever seen. Well, the craziest thing I've seen tonight.

Outside the club at the end of the night, I see the girl with her scooter and ask what happened to her. "I broke my leg. Here." She lifts her foot and points at her ankle, almost falling over. "This–," she pets the scooter, "thingy here is ever since my best friend. Better than any man. Takes me everywhere." She laughs too loud. "My mama didn't like the idea. No, no." She wiggles her finger, I assume mimicking her mother. "But the ceiling fell on my head at home, if you know what I mean. I had bumblebees in my butt. I wanted to be with my friends." She throws her arms out and ends up hanging around my neck. I have no idea what she means, but I try and hold her steady until she climbs off me.

"That's awesome. I wish I had done something like that when I got hurt a while back."

"So much fun. Best idea ever. Take that, Mama!" She yells and gives me a high five before heading off with her friends.

"Emily, do you want to go on a bike tour on Monday with the guys?" Amber asks me on the way back to the hostel.

"Well, after the one I did in Amsterdam, I'm not sure bikes are my thing." A bike tour? Anything but a bike tour. How am I going to get out of this?

"Oh, come on, you'll be with us. We can all be slow together," Jen offers in support.

"Okay, let me check. I might have a tour on Monday, but I don't remember what time."

I'm relieved to realize I already have a tour arranged at the same time, saving me from having to talk my way out of the bike tour. We all go out to dinner that night since it's the last night in Berlin for Amber and me. The two of them tell me about the great time they had, until it started to rain.

In the morning, we all say good-bye and exchange information. I get a last-minute pep talk about how wonderful South Africa will be from the beautiful scenery to the amazing animals.

Chapter 10

I've been out of work for months since the accident, even my close friends from work have faded away. However, my managing partner sends an e-mail each Saturday morning to check on me. I usually send back a vague response with a medical update, letting him know how beat up I am and that I'm still out of commission. He never asks me about coming back to work, but I feel confident that he'll bring me back. Heck, he made sure my insurance and benefits continued all this time, even though I wasn't working and I never promised to come back.

"Bruce Katz," crackles over the phone when he answers.

"Hi, Bruce, it's Emily." I put on my cheery but professional voice that got me noticed by him in the first place.

"Emily, it's wonderful to hear from you. I was just going to send you an e-mail. Not surprising you would beat me to it." He really seems surprised and happy to hear from me.

"You always told me to stay one step ahead of the boss." I hear him chuckle in response. "The reason I'm calling is that I think I'm about ready to return to work and I'm hoping you still have a place for me."

"Of course, we've all been waiting for you to be ready. I'll be honest–we didn't pay your benefits only out of the goodness of our hearts. We hoped you'd come back."

I almost feel guilty for doubting him after he says such nice things.

"The only thing is that I'm still in physical therapy and still seeing doctors every so often. Also, I'm not walking that well, so I won't be able to work as much as I did before, at least not at first. I'm willing to work from home, if need be."

Ugh. I know I sound like that annoying employee with a bunch of excuses that I used to ridicule. I'm sure I'll hear about how I came back to only work half as much as everyone else and then they'll think I want sympathy because I have some scar on my face. Maybe going back to work was a bad idea. But I need to start earning some money and being a part of society.

"I understand that, and we want to be there to support you in any way we can. I'll talk to the other partners; we'll work out something that will meet everyone's needs, at least until you're stronger. You're still on the island, right?"

I wonder how Bruce describes stronger. The doctors think I'll always have a limp, and the soreness is terrible when the weather is bad. The limp and pain should fade, but may last the rest of my life.

"Yes, I'm still here with my parents. When we realized how long I would need help, it didn't make sense to keep my apartment in the city. I hope I can move back soon." I still miss my little place a few blocks from work.

His voice gets soft when he offers, "Maybe we can get car service for the first few days to help with the transition."

"That would be amazing, not that there is anything wrong with the Long Island Rail Road, but it does make for a long day and I tire quickly." I sigh in relief. I've been exhausted just thinking about taking the train.

"I'm sure you know that all of your cases were reassigned. I'm not sure I can get you working on any of them again, but we have plenty of work to do here."

"I figured, but I really just want to get out and work my brain again before it turns to mush. All those drugs took a toll on me."

We laugh, neither one of us mentioning the few gibberish e-mails I sent to him after the accident.

He clears his voice, obviously done with the joking. "When do you want to start?"

"How about a week from Monday?" I don't like the doubt I hear in my voice. The old me would have sounded confident, like the answer was obvious. Instead, I sound weak, as though I don't know when I want to return, even though that's why I called.

"A week from Monday it is! I'll be in touch next week after I speak to the partners. We will all be happy to have you back."

"Thanks, Bruce. I appreciate all that you and the firm have done for me."

After saying our good-byes, I do a little happy dance. As good as they've been to me, I wasn't sure what to expect; they could have sent me on my way. Thankfully, they wanted me back as much as I wanted to go back.

I thought since I was already in Europe the flight to South Africa would be shorter. I was wrong. Getting to the airport in the afternoon and not arriving until the following morning makes me thankful for all those airline miles I earned so that I can now sit in the front of the plane, sleep, and have more privacy. When I finally board the plane, I find myself next to a man twenty years older than I. He's in casual designer clothing and has a little speckling of salt and pepper hair. After putting his bag in the overhead bin, he sits with a noticeable level of aggravation rolling off him.

When the flight attendant comes around with drinks, he takes a champagne, barely mumbles a thank-you, and quickly downs the drink.

"Are you going to Johannesburg for business or pleasure?" he abruptly asks me as he lowers his glass.

"Um, pleasure. I'm going to be touring around South Africa for the next few weeks."

"The country is great, but I wouldn't spend too much time in Joburg, it's not safe." He sits back as though he'd like to relax but doesn't know how.

"Yes, I've heard to be careful, avoid carrying a bag, don't go out after dark." The list of recommendations I got is endless.

"Yup, it's all true. I got carjacked there twice a long time ago. Once from my own driveway. After that, I spend as little time there as possible. Don't leave *anything* out if you're driving. That's how I got carjacked the second time; I stupidly had my briefcase on the seat next to me. Getting off the highway I stopped at a stop sign. Next thing I know I have a gun to my head." He's brown eyes are so intense when he says that, it's unnerving.

"There also isn't too much for a tourist to do. But the dollar will go far. You might want to hire a driver; he can keep you out of trouble and tell you a little bit about the city. Then head down to Cape Town."

"Yes, I'll be going there next. It does seem like there is more to do there." I'm getting scared by all this negativity.

"Cape Town isn't perfect, but there's more to do for a tourist, and the crime isn't as bad either. During the day, you can walk around most areas by yourself and you won't have any trouble. But in Johannesburg, you must be careful. A lot of my friends left years ago because the violence was so bad." His voice is stern, reminds me a bit of a mean teacher's voice.

"What brings you to Johannesburg?" The more he talks, I wonder why he's bothering to go there.

He shrugs as he lifts a stack of paper in his hands. "Work. I come a couple times a year. If I'm here over the weekend, I fly down to Cape Town."

"Do you have any other tips for me?" My fingers are crossed that he doesn't tell me more ways I could get into trouble—or hurt.

"Yes, go out and have a steak or something. Seriously, they grow the animals for meat more naturally, fewer hormones and stuff. I've never had a bad dinner in South Africa. Try something unusual like Kudu. You'll pay half the price you would at home and it will taste twice as good." His eyes light up with the talk of food.

The conversation dies after that, and I sleep most of the flight to Johannesburg. It's a restless sleep because I have at least one dream of being robbed. At least I didn't wake up screaming or anything; that would be awkward. And probably bad for my flying reputation.

There's no more discussion in the morning when breakfast is served before we arrive. We share a halfhearted good-bye when we disembark the plane. After clearing through the border and customs, I'm excited to see a man with my name on a sign waiting for me.

Ben is very nice and explains a little about the country as he takes me to the hotel. He also tells me that his company does tours around Johannesburg from the hotel if I'm interested. I suspect he's not trying to trick me since he tells me the concierge will make the arrangements for me, but I'm suspicious.

When I meet with the concierge, he offers me a group tour to the Apartheid Museum in the afternoon, which I sign up for. However, for the following morning, he can only offer me a private tour of Soweto or Pretoria, and I'm feeling skittish about being alone with someone here. I decide that a quiet morning before my flight to Cape Town is the better option. I really haven't taken much time to rest. The concierge is a bit pushy about it, telling me it's a great opportunity and not to waste my time in the hotel when I'm on holiday. I ignore him and head to my room to repack my day bag so I only have the essentials I need for the afternoon. Mini Eve is left behind in the room because she's not essential for the tour and I would be sad if I lost her. I'm in the lobby with the other two people on my tour when Ben arrives to take us to the Apartheid Museum.

Ben gives us some history of apartheid, telling us some of the key names to look for. He grew up being taught that white people were superior to non-whites. However, he knew so many sweet and nurturing black people that he knew there was no difference between the races. When he had the chance, he voted to repeal apartheid.

"You can't imagine the lines, they went on forever. I'd never seen anything like it. It didn't stop anyone either. They waited, some more than a day. One woman died while waiting, that's how important the vote was."

I remember this as I walk through the museum and see the images of the lines, people waiting for hours to end the oppression. The commitment is heartwarming to see. I sniffle a bit as I try to keep from crying. I'm not sure if it's the level of dedication by a society to end the oppression of one group that moves me or something else.

As I continue through the museum, I see the violence of people fighting for freedom, of the men who died fighting, particularly of those whose cause of death was hidden for years. Their names temporarily erased from history and from the honor they deserved. It's sad to see that their sacrifice was intentionally hidden. The museum brings that dignity back to them.

Even after the end of apartheid, the country had so much healing to do, something that is so often overlooked. It's easy to glue things back together, but the fusion takes time and help from the right people. Nelson Mandela was one of the most important of those. He fought back his own fears to lead people toward unity.

The four of us meet at the museum entrance for our ride back to the hotel. Ben takes us for a ride by Nelson Mandela's house in Soweto. The road is littered with tin shack homes covered in graffiti. It's possibly the most depressing site I've ever seen. Children wander between the homes, some staring through the fence as the cars drive by. Rows and rows of shacks the size of my bedroom at home. I've never witnessed such poverty, not even close. Ben explains that those areas are not part of the township, but rather feed off the township. The people living there are waiting for homes to be built. It's a slow process, but one that is improving the lives of millions.

In the meantime, conditions in the communities are terrible. There are no organized government services, no official utilities. Crime is rampant. It sends a shiver through me at the thought of living in those conditions. Even just driving by increases my fear. I think of the worst areas of New York City but nothing touches this.

I'm feeling hyper-alert and fidgety by the time we get to the area where Nelson Mandela's house is. I'm relieved to see small but sturdy homes in the area. It seems more normal here, and although the homes are small, they are cared for. As for Nelson Mandela's home, it is modest, befitting the man he was.

When Ben drops us at the hotel, I see the concierge, who offers me the morning tour of Pretoria again. This time the guide is offering a discount on the price he had earlier. It's apparent they think I don't want to do the tour because of the price, and no matter how many times I say no, they tell me what a good price they are offering. I'm already feeling emotional and know tears aren't terribly far away after my emotional afternoon. I can't take the pressure. After what feels like the hundredth time, I yell at the man and storm away toward my room to hide. It's the last bit of strength left in me. The strength slowly evaporates as I walk to my room and feel tears dropping from my eyes. I'm not sure why. I'm not sad or angry, just frustrated.

When I come down to the hotel restaurant for dinner, I find myself sneaking to avoid the concierge. I don't want to deal with him anymore. His intentions may be good, but he's made me feel uncomfortable. Fortunately, I don't see him for the rest of the night or the next day until it's time to leave for the airport. I'm happy to see that it's Ben driving me back to the airport for my flight to Cape Town.

Along the way, Ben assures me that Cape Town is safer and has more things to do. That sentiment is shared by my seatmate on the flight. He agrees that Johannesburg has its problems, but is much better than it had been in the 90's. But Cape Town is another story. He doesn't tell me not to go out at night, but does caution me to take a taxi if I do. And he tells me that if I find a township tour, take it. It will give a better idea of what it's like to live there.

When I arrive at the hotel that evening, I'm greeted by another concierge who is as helpful as the one in Johannesburg but not as pushy. There are also several people at the hotel who will be on the tour that I'm taking in a few days. He easily convinces me to take a tour the following day of the Cape Peninsula and then a wine tour the day after. All are with smaller groups so there will be plenty of attention given to us.

The Cape Peninsula tour includes a visit to Robben Island, with one of the roughest boat rides I've ever taken. I'm afraid we were going to end up like the SS *Minnow*. Once we're on the island, the tour is amazing. Although the bus tour isn't the most exciting, it's the only chance to see the whole island, including the lime quarry where the prisoners worked and some of the solitary confinement cells are. The second half of the tour is done by a former prisoner.

As we tour the prison, he explains how Mandela had to build his own prison block, which we eventually get to see. Mandela's cell is a small room with a mattress roll, a table, and a view of a small courtyard. It makes the hospital room I spent weeks in look like a house. Our guide tells us about his own experience here. I marvel at the human spirit, how a man who was sent to prison because he fought for his freedom can return years later to teach others about the experience. He spent most of his time in larger communal cells, which allowed him to work with others in the movement to end apartheid. Funny how so many men were put here as punishment for fighting apartheid, only to bring them together in one place where they could continue the fight.

The guide and former prisoner leaves me a little shaken. I had complained about how I was stuck at home and in hospitals for months after the accident. But I had TV, visitors, books, and a cell phone with the Internet. I might have been broken and drugged up, but I was relatively comfortable. The prisoners had a room and maybe some people to talk to. I feel some of his pain at the lost years away from his family. Knowing that not all his family supported his political activism and that his children lost years with him. He still fought against not just apartheid, but the voices telling him to fight for his family and his nation.

I think about the kids at the Johannesburg Township, standing behind a fence and watching the world pass while they wait for the government to build the family a house. Those are the kids my guide fought for. I wonder whether they have a better life.

As for the rest of Cape Town, it's amazing! Even though most of the bad things I heard about South Africa were focused on Johannesburg, the truth is that most people I know have no idea where Johannesburg and Cape Town are and what makes them unique. But Cape Town is gorgeous with magnificent views of the Atlantic and Indian Oceans.

Our guide warns us the baboons are dangerous, but they're so cute that I have trouble believing it. Until I see one trying to get into a car parked on the street. The baboon stretches and pulls on the door. When the first door doesn't work, he tries another. A man comes running out of the gift shop to his nearby car yelling at the baboon. The baboon looks at him and tries another door, when that doesn't work he reaches through the car window and steals a bag of potato chips, then slowly walks away. On the one hand, it's the craziest thing I've seen; on the other, it's hysterical to watch this man screaming and running at the baboon who just stares back. Fortunately, the man stopped before he got too close to the baboon. They've been known to attack tourists who get too close.

The rest of the tour involves seeing penguins. They're nestled in an alcove surrounded by giant boulders. The sand is light brown and calm turquoise water lightly rolls up on the beach. It looks like a photoshopped postcard.

After my first full day in Cape Town, I can honestly say I'm in love. The city is so beautiful and I got a glimpse of how many layers there are to its personality. The social cues are different; therefore, I'm still cautious. But I can't help to feel anything other than the warmth from the locals I've met along the way.

Chapter 11

"Emily, I thought you had plans with someone from work tonight?" Jessica asks as she breezes into the house on a Saturday night.

"I canceled. The last time I went out with this girl she acted like I was made of porcelain or she was oblivious to my being slower than I used to be."

"So what? I do that to you all the time," she says as she unpacks some bags for my parents.

"At least I can say something to you without you getting offended. I just feel abandoned when she does it." The last time I was out with Alexa, one of our secretaries at work, she wanted to help me get out of the car, but then left me to be almost be trampled when we were inside the restaurant. She was totally unaware of how crowded the lobby was and how many people bumped me while we waited. I was frustrated by the time we got a table.

During Jessica's silence, I get a text message from Alexa asking if I'm feeling okay. I ignore it because it will just prompt her to chat about work. Jessica doesn't miss my action, or my inaction, and starts peppering me about why I'm ignoring people from work. "Jess, I'm tired of talking to them."

She raises her eyebrows and stares at me.

"They either talk about work and avoid mentioning Dag in obvious ways, or they're complaining about first-world problems. Their computer is broken, they have to work too many hours, the cleaning lady is sick and they have to clean their own bathroom. Meanwhile, I wish I was able clean a bathroom." The list of complaints is long, and I can't sympathize with any of it.

It just makes me angrier.

"Emily, at least they're trying to connect with you. Have some patience with them. They might not be doing it right, but they're trying. All you do is sit and complain about everyone and everything." She ends her lecture with an exaggerated sigh at the end and purses her lips.

"Jess, when you go through half of what I've been through, let me know how much patience you have."

Jessica opens her mouth to say something, then stops herself and leaves the room.

After a few days alone in Cape Town, I'm finally meeting up with the group for my tour through South Africa and to Zimbabwe. The first two people I meet are Laura and Adam, a husband and wife, on a two-week vacation. At first they seem very nice, but it doesn't take long to realize something isn't quite right. Over dinner and after dinner drinks, I realize that something is weird. Adam seems more like a father figure than a husband. As our conversation continues, I hear that Laura's mother died when Laura was seven. It was a tragic accident: her father accidentally knocked her mother down the stairs. I can't help wondering what role that played in Laura's relationship with Adam. I can't figure this out in one night, but I suspect I'll learn more before the end of the tour.

After they leave, James, another member of the group, tries to expand his drinking circle. He graduated from college a year ago, and I don't think working in the tech field has helped him grow emotionally. While he seems immature for his age, he also seems to drift and accept whatever life offers him. He's very lighthearted and completely different from me.

"Come on, Emily, just one more drink. We're having fun," he whines when I get up to leave.

"We have two weeks together to have fun."

"Yeah, but think of how much better it will be when you know me better." He has this adorable pleading tone that probably works well in a college bar. It has no effect on me.

"We'll get along better if I get some rest. Have a good night." I know his type; doesn't think you can be having fun unless you're drunk. It's been a while since I dealt with someone like this, but I'm sure I'll manage for two weeks. At least he'll be fun most of the time. Or he'll be hungover and sleepy.

When I get to my room, my roommate Hana is getting ready for bed. She's a dark-haired, light-skinned girl from Ireland, who works as a nurse in Galway. Aside from my difficulty understanding her strong accent, she seems like a good roommate. That's nice because we'll be sharing a room for the next two weeks.

The following morning twelve of us meet in the hotel dining room for breakfast and a tour of Cape Town. Because most of the group has been in Cape Town, our guide, Sharon, moves us at a slower pace, giving us the opportunity to get to know each other better.

We finally meet Sue, who missed the group at dinner last night because her cage diving tour ran late. When I finally get a chance to ask her about it at lunch, I find myself a little jealous. I considered for an instant going cage diving, but between the price and the sharks I decide not to. From talking to her, the shark issue sounds minimal, while the risk of throwing up is ninety-nine percent. I guess I should save money and my stomach.

"You should really do it; it is sooo much fun. We were bouncing around in the water, it was crazy. Then a shark would swim by and we would dunk under the water until we needed to breathe again. We did it over and over until everyone got tired." She's practically bouncing in her seat with excitement as she talks about it.

"How close did the sharks get?" I wonder if they get close enough to touch the cages.

"Close enough to see them, but not so close that you thought they were going to attack the cage. The guys on the boat would try to bring them in at an angle so they swam by the corners of the cage. It actually looked worse from the boat than from the cage." She should do TV ads for the company, because she's so convincing.

"Isn't the water cold?" I continue.

"Yes, but not terrible! You're in such a rush getting into the water that there is no time to think about it until you're already in the water. You just do it."

It sounds like torture. I can barely get into my parent's pool when the water is under 80°.

Wade, who is also sitting with us, chimes in that he didn't have time to do cage diving, but he did it years ago when he was in Australia. "It's worth the experience to do it at least once. I would have done it here, but I didn't have the time. There aren't many experiences like it."

Wade is the elder of the group. I think he's about forty while the rest of the group is in their twenties and maybe early thirties. I was seated next to him on the bus in the morning, and he spends a lot of his free time adjusting things on his camera. When I finally inquired about it, he tells me he does side work as a photographer in Denmark, for a company just outside Copenhagen. He's using his vacation hoping to get photos of the Big Five and a sunny day at Victoria Falls. While we talk, he tells me that although the rhinoceros is nearing extinction, the leopards might be harder to spot because of their size and color. He assures me that on his last trip he saw several lions, elephants, and cape buffalo.

In the evening, the group goes to dinner at the home of a resident in a township in Cape Town. I'm a little nervous about this since I'm used to eating in restaurants, not going to random people's houses for dinner. In addition, we're traveling to a mysterious township that I've heard so much bad stuff about. I'm a little freaked. Our driver is very nice and tells us a little about the family we'll be eating with. A husband and wife with three children. The wife's sister and mother may be there to help cook too.

When we arrive, I'm reminded of my grandmother's home; the fixtures, furniture, and appliances are old but functional. Most of the furniture matches, but there are a few odd pieces, I suspect to make the home more comfortable when they bring in groups for dinner. I quickly find myself studying the floors. Without layers of polyurethane, the natural grains of the wood are visible. I never realized how beautiful a natural wood floor could be when you strip off its protective barrier.

For dinner, we have tripe with potatoes and fried onions while the family tells us a little about food and life in Cape Town. While it's obvious they struggle, there is an overwhelming feeling that they are doing much better today than they would have if the country hadn't ended apartheid.

There's a strong level of community today. The friends they bought the house from lowered the price of the house for them, and their family helped them with the extra money they needed to buy the house. It was important to them that they have a chance to improve their lives. As dinner winds down, a neighbor stops by with our dessert, malva pudding. When she comes in, she starts asking a lot of questions of everyone in the group, making me wonder whether she makes the malva pudding as an excuse to meet the guests. I would feel like we were part of a show, except she seems genuinely curious about us and the places we live, as we are of them.

Matt, from our tour, asks many questions of the family. I feel like he memorized the Wikipedia page about South Africa and is testing the authenticity by asking this very nice family about things. Never mind that he keeps asking questions about other parts of the country and the family keeps saying they've never left Cape Town. I groan with each succeeding question, even trying to change the conversation once. Thankfully, their six-year-old daughter comes out of her hiding spot to the main room to dance around for her new audience. She has chestnut eyes that look like they've never known a boundary in her life. By the time we leave, I'm left with a new appreciation of community.

The following morning the tour leaves for Johannesburg and arrives in the early afternoon, just in time for an afternoon tour that takes us through some not-so-nice areas of the city. I'm not excited to be back, even though we do have different activities planned from what I did here a few days ago. Our guide explains that although there was a spike in crime, it's lower now, and people just need to follow some common-sense tips. No matter what our guide says, I still can't shake the uneasy feeling I have about Johannesburg.

It seems that Matt is in his element again, asking our guide too many questions. Our last stop on the tour is a visit to a youth program. We park our van near a deserted building, and our guide walks us along a dirt path between a fence and some railroad tracks. The farther we walk, the more trash there is along the path—as well as a dead mouse. After the path bends we see some small groups of kids playing, with adults chatting nearby. Our guide obviously knows the area well and walks us around with enough confidence for me to follow, even though I feel completely out of my element.

We crawl through an opening in a fence, which surprisingly seems the safest option for this visit. Inside we are greeted by some children and teens who are excited to tell us about their home. The center is arranged with several small buildings around a small courtyard. They have bedrooms for girls and boys, and several common rooms. Because we arrive as the sun is setting, we're guided through some of the areas quickly. With limited electricity, only a few rooms have light, the rest are in the dark.

The main common room has lights, and a few kids are playing board games. The room reminds me of a child's version of a college apartment. There is a lot of hand-me-down furniture. The room feels enormous with several different sections for kids of various ages. There are books everywhere. It reminds me of a nursery school with so many books.

Just as I'm mulling over that thought I overhear Laura telling Adam that she's surprised they have a television, that she was expecting them to be poor here. His response is, "And they have books. Maybe they can learn to read and have a chance to get out of this place. I mean, really, these kids don't have much of a chance in life."

"You're right, geez. I wouldn't last here five minutes," Laura responds.

While I'm looking at pictures of kids who have graduated from the school, the lights go out, telling us that the tour is finished. On our way out, the walk in the dark back to our van doesn't seem scary.

We spend the night in a posh B&B, a clear contrast to the youth center we visited—including the high walls that protect us from the animals in the area. The host family are hunters, with animal heads lining the walls of their living and dining rooms. Dinner is served with a giant giraffe head watching over us. I name the giraffe Rasputin, and I'm sure he's giving the group a dirty look as we eat meat with our dinner.

James seems to like Rasputin and his animal head friends, and he wants to stay out with them longer. Although I have no interest in staying with animal heads, I do stay after dinner for drinks. This gives us the chance to hear stories from our hosts. Xavier speaks so eloquently of animal hunts. The pleasure of spending time outside with no distractions from TV, phone, or computer. Then, finding a spot to hide or track the animals. Often, he would just watch the animal wander by without being noticed. He always had a goal for the day and never hunted an animal just because it was fun. He took those opportunities to watch nature happen. Maybe the animal wandered by, but he also saw some animals fight. On one or two occasions he saw a pair mating. Sometimes an animal would watch him for a while, trying to decide whether he was a tree or a person. Once, he was attacked by a squirrel. When Matt asks about poaching, Xavier rants about how much he hates poachers and all the ways we can help end poaching.

If I thought we had been up early to drive from Johannesburg to Kruger National Park, perhaps my view on mornings would change by going on safari. Up and out of the hotel before dawn with a bag of food for breakfast. The group uses two safari vehicles for the day. My truck includes Laura, Adam, Wade, James, and Hana. I haven't seen James more sober and awake in the morning, all he wants to see are some rhino before they become extinct. Our guide for the day, Micky, explains how not to get eaten by an animal. Apparently it's easy: stay in the vehicle.

Wade is seated in front of me and has enough camera equipment for all of us. I thought I had seen all his equipment, but today he brought out an extra camera, a monopod, and, he assures me, three battery packs. I'm not sure where he carries all this stuff. He's a slim, tall man. Where does he hide it all?

"Wade, what's the thing on top of the camera?" I ask about some box-like thing.

"A wildlife fill flash. Helps to get better pictures. I've used it around the world, great investment!" he gleefully asserts.

Who knew they made such a device? Meanwhile, I realize that Laura and Adam are talking about him behind me. Eventually Laura leans forward and asks me what the deal is with all of Wade's stuff.

"He's a photographer," I answer.

"Ohhhhh, that's explains a lot. I was starting to think he was a weirdo since he wouldn't leave his backpack alone for thirty seconds. And the constant picture taking . . . we'll probably stay here all day. And what's that thing on his camera now?" She rambles her thoughts.

Did she just ask about being here all day? Isn't that why we're here? I keep most of that to myself. "Laura, it's some sort of flash for his pictures. Aren't you excited to see the animals?"

"Well, yes, of course, but I also wanted to rest some too. It's been go-go-go every day. I think I need a break. We are on vacation after all."

"You'll be fine. I think Sharon said we had the option to go out tomorrow or stay at the hotel. You can rest tomorrow if you want." Adams rubs her back as he explains the trip itinerary to her as if she were child.

"Adam, did you see how Sue is dressed? I don't think she even brought a jacket with her. She must be freezing. Why didn't she check the weather before she came? She seems like a bright girl, but who knows," Laura interjects.

On the way to the park we are all freezing in the soft-top safari vehicle that doesn't seem to have a heater. These small yet annoying conversations continue all day and through lunch. I wish I could get away from the group for a bit.

At lunch our guide tells us about how dangerous some of the animals are, even telling us about a friend who got scratched by a leopard she was working with. That somehow prompts Laura to ask me, "Is that what happened to your face?"

The group gets deadly silent, and everyone's heads swirl to Laura, who seems oblivious to the looks she's getting and the silence around her.

"No, Laura, I was in a car accident," I manage to say with a clear voice, and while I know I should be annoyed with her, I want to laugh at her. We had discussed my car accident the first day the group was together.

"Oh, that's right, I totally forgot about that."

I notice a trace of a valley girl accent when she speaks. "Is there anything you can do to get it fixed?" she asks next. "No, Laura, it's already fixed." At another time, I think this conversation would have bothered me, but today it just feels like I'm dealing with someone so unaware of their surroundings that they have no idea that the question is rude. The rest of the day passes quickly as we find giraffes, hippos, elephants, and catch an amazing sunset on the way back to the hotel. James got to see his rhino too.

The following few days are wonderful, even if they mean I have no break from this large group. I'm not used to groups after traveling by myself for so long. We head north to Zimbabwe and see the Great Zimbabwe Monument and ruins. As we discuss the historical significance of the area and the size of the ruins, we end up discussing Egypt, where the largest ruins on the continent are.

While Wade regales us with tales of his visit there a few months ago, he assures us that he felt perfectly safe and that it was nice because there were so few tourists. He encourages Hana, Sue, James, and me to consider going. Wade's a sweet guy, who has traveled a lot, and although I'm not ready to go to Egypt now, I appreciate the way he's encouraging us not to be afraid to go.

After several minutes of discussing where to go in Egypt, Matt overhears our conversation and interrupts. "I went there years ago, before all that trouble there. You couldn't pay me enough money to go there now," he tells us with disgust.

Wade calmly responds as though Matt might have missed what he said. "I was there a few months ago. It was great, I would go back in an instant."

"I heard you say that, but you're not an American. They hate the Americans there now, and with the government unstable, you never know what could happen." He seems annoyed that someone would contradict him.

Wade murmurs, "I was with a group of Americans; they weren't treated any differently from me or the other Europeans. After talking to my group, I realize the media really hypes smaller things that have nothing to do with the tourism industry."

"Well, I wasn't comfortable when I was there years ago–all that offering to buy the girls for millions of camels. It was so weird and rude to the girls. They laughed it off, but it was creepy." Matt seems more disgusted the more he talks about it.

Wade drops the topic. I can tell he's getting tired of Matt's outbursts. As for the rest of us, we start to laugh quietly. We've heard enough of Matt's ramblings to know he has a distorted vision of the world and doesn't like to be told he's wrong. Matt doesn't laugh; he just sits sullenly.

The next leg of our trip starts with an evening drive to a hotel closer to the border into Zimbabwe at Beit Bridge. If my friends at home were paying attention, they would have been more concerned about this crossing than the crime and violence in Johannesburg.

Apparently, Beit Bridge is the busiest border in Africa–with the chaos to match it. Even with the conveniences of a tour group, we are up early to beat the lines at the border. On the way, we were warned that anything could happen, including getting past the border in under an hour, or over six hours. Sharon asks us to be on our best behavior, stay calm, and avoid anything that will bring attention to ourselves. In the meantime, she will take care of most of the work. Sharon does such a great job that we get through the border in two hours. Looking at some of the travelers around us, two hours seems like a miracle.

As the day drags, I sense a cold coming on. It will probably dominate my moods for the next few days as we head through the Great Zimbabwe Monument and on to see more wildlife at Matobo National Park. I'm so congested, and headachy that I either miss our activities or am too tired to enjoy them.

On the way to Victoria Falls, I'm still congested and loopy. I find myself constantly drifting off to sleep until I wake in the back of the van to the distant sound of thunder. I'm able to peek a few glimpses of the falls through trees; at least I think that is what I see. Meanwhile, Sharon explains to us about the falls being the biggest in the world. She supports that with a bunch of statistics that put me to sleep. I wake just as the van parking near the falls so we can walk to our first full view. My only comparison is Niagara Falls, and that was twenty or so years ago, but these are magnificent. The colors are gorgeous, and the spray of water creates small rainbows in different spots. Even the roar the water makes is impressive.

I'm not sure how long we stay–long enough for me to take a bunch of pictures of the falls. When I go through my pictures, I discover that I even took one of my little Eve doll with the falls behind her. I don't remember taking that picture.

Without any issues, we make our way to Zambia and our hotel in Livingston. As much as I want to sleep, I pull myself together to meet the group for our last dinner. Everyone is very chatty, even though a few people seem to be coming down with the cold too. At least it's the end of their trip and their colds won't ruin it. Over dinner we discuss what we loved most about the trip and what we didn't like; then we take pictures of each other together and thank Sharon for all her hard work keeping us together and on time.

As exhausted as I am at the end of this part of the journey, I am also excited about how much I saw in a little over two weeks in Africa. I'll miss the way the group provided a network to look out for each other and make little things easier. No trying to find my way to a hotel on public transportation I have never been on. No navigating a difficult border. I still like my freedom, but I also appreciated having someone take care of me. Over the next day and a half, I say good-bye to everyone, some I will gladly hear from again, others I will grudgingly add as Facebook friends.

Chapter 12

" Emily, it's been about a year. I've seen your x-rays, and I still see quite a bit of scar tissue in your ankle. Are you still in pain?"

"Yes, it's not as bad as it was, but it's still painful. I'm either trying not to walk or I'm finding myself walking funny to avoid the pain. I tried physical therapy again, but it didn't help. I stopped and came here."

"That's what I figured. Dr. Max and reviewed the physical therapy notes together with the older x-rays, and he agrees that the next step will be surgery." He pauses for a moment before continuing. "Don't look so worried. This surgery will be significantly easier than the ones you had in the past."

"How or why did this happen?" Is this really happening? Why is this happening? What did I do to deserve this torture?

"It's not terribly uncommon, but the lack of mobility you had after the initial surgeries allowed the scar tissue to form. When we go back in, we clean out the scar tissue, then we get you up and moving so it doesn't have a chance to form again."

I close my eyes and sigh loudly at the news. "I just can't deal with doing all that again."

"I know, Emily; it's been a lot. The good news is that this is a relatively minor procedure, especially compared to everything else you've done. The recovery, aside from having to do some more physical therapy, will be easy for you. After you'll be feeling much better, have better movement, and you won't hurt the rest of your leg by walking funny."

The next few days are a bit of a blur as I head to Namibia for a week. A friend from college encouraged me to go there for scenery. Going was not one of my better decisions. How hard could it be to travel from Victoria Falls to Namibia? After all, Zambia and Namibia are near each other. However, when I was planning how to get to Namibia I was given the choice of spending several hundred dollars for two days of flying or spend twenty hours on a bus for forty dollars. I don't know how that is possible, but the flight connections were terrible. At least I had time to mentally prepare myself to be on a bus for twenty hours. There's a lesson on planning ahead that I'm sure I'll apply in the future. The upside to having a cold on a twenty-hour bus ride is that people tend to avoid you.

The bus ride to Namibia is long, but the country offers something special. The game drives are different from what I had experienced in South Africa; they're shorter and earlier in the morning. Shorter is nice; the early mornings were starting to grow old. Aren't I on vacation? As I watch a cheetah stalk its prey, I giggle a little inside thinking of that scene in *Armageddon* when Ben Affleck is playing with the animal crackers on Liv Tyler's stomach. As unique as it is to see a cheetah, the real reason I came to Namibia is for the dunes.

I laugh, along with the other members of the group I'm touring with, as we try to sand surf on the dunes, then bounce through a 4x4 ride on another set. The dunes are quite different from all the other places I have been. Although there is plenty of sand at the beach, it's not like this. The colors are darker and the texture thicker compared to the sand I'm used to. The sand extends to the horizon in some places, all a brown rolling landscape.

The setting sun is my favorite part. I've seen the sun set in a lot of places, but this is special—the way the sun hits the dunes and the way the colors are reflected. The brown sand gets darker and more golden as the orange sky glows over it as the sun lowers. For a few minutes, nothing matters. Not Dagobert, not the twenty-hour bus ride, not the scar on my face, not my leg pain. It's just tranquility.

It can't last, good things must come to an end, but, at least, this will end with an easier trip out of Africa as I head to Rome for some pasta and history.

Or so I thought. It takes two flights and twenty hours to get to Rome. When I arrive, my annoyance at the long flights quickly fades.

After collecting my luggage, I follow the signs for the airport shuttle bus. Although the train is faster, the bus costs significantly less. Because I'm arriving before my apartment host will be ready, I don't rush. The bus drops me off outside a chaotic Termini Station. I still have time before I can meet my host so I take a leisurely walk with my luggage and watch all the different people I pass. The walk by the Pantheon excites me when I realize I am in one of the most beautiful, famous, and oldest cities in the world.

Then I enter one of the most famous churches in the world. The Pantheon has Raphael's tomb. I'm sad to realize he died so young, unable to marry the love of his life. Nearby, I stumble upon Piazza Navona. It's alive with people, mostly tourists, and, of course, plenty of peddlers selling knock-off designer bags of all shapes and sizes. I overhear a father telling his kids about the fountain that was in the *Da Vinci Code*. Everywhere I look there is something interesting: a sign, a fountain, a lost tourist.

Just before lunch, I meet with my host, Siena, and I am welcomed heartily into her apartment, where she rents a spare bedroom and bathroom. The location is excellent, and although more expensive than the hostels that weren't nearly as close to the amazing sites, it's much nicer. Siena offers me a few suggestions for different activities I can do to take advantage of my time in Rome.

After showing me the apartment, she takes me to lunch at a local spot. If I turn in my seat I can see the Pantheon. Siena talks to me about life in Rome, and I get to eat surrounded by locals, instead of at one of the many tourist traps that are so prevalent in the area.

After lunch, I head to the Colosseum. Despite the long line to get in, and the heat, the Colosseum is amazing. From pictures, the size of it is hard to realize, but I'm sad that it seems to need a lot of work, just to keep it safe for tourists to visit. There are quite a few areas that are sectioned off to keep the tourists away.

As I roam the streets, it feels great to be back in Europe, even if the language is different. There's something about it, maybe being able to read body language better and feeling like I can blend in with the locals. Of course, the streets are lined with tourists, but there are many locals strolling their way to dinner or walking home for work. I marvel at the city; around every corner there's a monument to something in a quaint little square with tourists, lovers, and families passing by.

As the sun sets, I notice my stomach growling. I quickly find a nice café with an amazing view, and even though I know I'll be overpaying for average food, it doesn't matter. I sit down, order, and enjoy people watching until my cell phone pings.

Text from Eve:
Are you alive? I think you got to Rome today? Or are you busying Roming . . .

Text to Eve:
I'm alive and I've been Roming all over Rome today. Just having dinner and staring at the Pantheon.

Text from Eve:
AWESOME, glad you're doing it right! How was Africa, and whatever country you were in? Zimibia?

I laugh at Eve's butchering of the country names while I wait for my food to arrive. I take the time while I'm eating to really enjoy the environment, the setting sun, the tourists with selfie sticks. I hope I'm not like the tourists with the selfie sticks. I see one of them hit someone else with the stick and almost cause a fight.

I reach for my purse and can't find it. My stomach drops. I frantically look everywhere around the table for my purse, under the table, under each chair. A chill spreads as the blood rushes from my face, from my whole body.

Where is my purse?

Did I bring my purse with me? Yes, I definitely had it with me, and I definitely don't have it with me now.

Where did I put it? The floor by my feet? Yes. No. I had it on the floor. Did I put it on the back of my chair after I put my phone back in? Argh, I put it on the back of the chair. I'm an idiot. And now some stupid Roman thief has my purse.

NO, NO, NO, NO, no, this is not happening to me!

What was in my purse? My wallet? I think. My phone? Yes, my phone. UGH. What else?

I'm not discreet as I peek under other guest's tables. When the waiter comes over, I mime what happened and give him the few euros from my pocket and beg for help. I want to get back to the apartment and decide what was in my purse–especially whether my passport was in it.

Please don't let my passport be in it. PLEASE!

As I speed walk like a New Yorker trying to catch a train, I catalogue what was in my purse: my phone, my wallet with some cash and a credit card, my last tube of Blistex, driver's license, pain medication, and I'm not entirely sure what else. Shoot, I think my little Eve doll was in there too. Not my Eve doll!

At least my keys to Siena's apartment are in my pocket, allowing me to burst through the door like a crazed American lawyer on a mission. Siena jumps up from the couch when she sees me and follows me to my room asking what's wrong. I think I yell about my purse as I rush into my room looking through my carry-on for what might be missing. Within thirty seconds my bag is strewn across the bed in a way that only makes sense to a hysterical person on a mission. Thankfully, I see my little plastic Eve lying on my bed with all my other stuff.

Siena is obviously much calmer than I am and can decipher my ramblings about my purse, phone, and passport.

"Ahhh, my passport, my sweet lovely passport." I kiss it and show it to Siena. It was in one of my other bags, along with some cash and my spare credit card.

Frustration and relief start to settle over me and I pull out my computer. I need to shut off my phone so some stupid Roman thief doesn't start calling Guam or somewhere else.

Eventually, Siena calms me down enough to convince me to make a police report. Why didn't I think of a police report? I am ready to run out the door at the mention of it. Siena stops me and says before going to the police I should have a list of items that were stolen. She will help me. The girl is brilliant. I don't know what I would do without her.

We go through my stuff a little more slowly. Siena makes a list, and I shut off my phone. Apparently, I didn't do it right the first time. Then Siena walks me back to the restaurant and explains to the manager what happened. The manager takes her phone number down in case someone turns in my purse or any of the items from it.

The next stop is the police station. She translates for me as we go through the process of making a report. When my brain starts to slow down and I realize that so many things are missing, my eyes start to fill with tears. I try to fight them off, telling myself there is no reason to cry and tears won't help me. But once one tear falls, the others come also. Siena offers me a tissue so that I'm not slobbering on myself. Holding the damp tissue in my hand reminds me that my own tissues were in my purse, a fact that only makes me cry more.

Back at Siena's place with a police report in hand, I still don't have a phone, but at least I have the extra emergency credit card I left in my suitcase and most of the cash I had taken out of the ATM after I arrived. I discover through all of this that it's amazingly easy to cancel my credit and bank cards and order replacements. All I needed were addresses to ship everything to. Replacing my phone will be more complicated.

I am lucky to reach Eve by Skype in the evening because she is often working. After I cry as I tell her my story, she reminds me that I have been through worse, much worse. I will figure it out, and she will help. My first order is to go to bed and get some rest while she researches what to do about the phone.

I wake the next morning puffy eyed and mentally drained, but thankful for Eve's thorough e-mail describing all my options to replace my phone. They're all expensive, but I decide a single woman running around the world shouldn't be without a phone for long. Ultimately, the security the phone gives me is worth more than the cost of a new phone. Or so my mother tells me in her e-mail after Eve told her what happened. Besides, I figure my stupid mistake has to have a cost, and in this case, it's the price of a new phone. I'm not sure the punishment is harsh enough, but I also haven't figured in the price of a new purse yet.

The more I think about it, the dumber I feel. I spent all that time in South Africa worried I would get robbed or carjacked and its Rome where I have my purse stolen because I'm too busy watching tourists to watch my own bag. After two months of traveling, I'm my own nemesis.

Conveniently, the tour I booked for that day is in the afternoon, giving me time to run around Rome and buy a new phone and SIM card so I can interact with the world again.

As I walk around Rome that afternoon on what is probably an excellent tour, I find myself constantly reaching for the purse I don't have. It's very unsettling, and the more I look for it, the more annoyed I become for having lost it.

When the tour ends, I quietly walk away, straight to a gelato stand where I buy the biggest cup of gelato they will sell me. I sit and gorge on it as people wander past. I feel pathetic, but I accept it.

Eventually, I motivate myself to shop for a new purse. Maybe the shopping will make me feel better, as will having a purse to put my things in. At the first few shops I can't find a thing that I like: it's either too expensive, too big, too small, too much like my old purse, not enough like my old purse. My pickiness starts to annoy me, so is my checking to make sure my new phone is in my pocket. In the tenth store, I find the perfect bag, except it's too expensive. More than I feel I deserve to spend on a purse after being so reckless with the first one. The sales woman really works on me to buy it, but I walk out empty-handed.

Two shops later, I find the perfect wallet; at least I have that to show for my shopping trip. I spend the better part of the night texting with Eve, telling her about how I had to abandon the perfect purse in the tenth shop and how I am never going to find something that I like at a reasonable price. It isn't long before my phone starts to ring with a call from my mother, not a frequent occurrence.

I barely get out, "Hi, Mom," before she interrupts.

"Just buy the stupid bag. I'll put money in your bank account tomorrow," she tells me in a clipped tone.

"No, Mom, I'll find something cheaper. It just gets beat up with all the traveling anyway."

"You have a ton of bags that cost twice as much in your closet. Buy the bag. Consider it a stop-torturing-yourself gift from your dad and me."

After I finally agree to take the money and promise to go buy the bag the following morning, we have a chance to catch up on everything that has happened in the past two weeks since we last spoke. I feel a little better and am hopeful the new bag will help too. I am even more excited when my replacement ATM and credit card show up the next day.

I make the best of my time in Rome. I'm almost afraid to take the new purse with me, and when I do, I'm very careful about making sure I only have the things I need. On my last day, I take a cooking class and learn how to make fresh pasta. Thinking of my life back home, I'm not sure when I would ever have a chance to make it, but I really hope I will be able to find the time.

Before leaving for Florence, Siena makes sure I have a tentative itinerary through the rest of Italy and helps me book tickets in Florence to see the *David* and the Duomo. She talks me out of going to Pisa. She starts by telling me that they are looking for easy victims there and someone will try to steal my purse again. I tell her I just won't bring it with me. But she convinces me when she shows me pictures of her trip to the Cinque Terre. I know I have to do that instead.

When I arrived at the Academia I was afraid seeing the *David* would be a disappointment, but he met every expectation. Down the long corridor of the Academia, he stands on a pedestal under a rotunda of light. Although the corridor is lined with Michelangelo's unfinished statuary, *David* grabs your attention. He commands the room like no other piece of art I've ever seen, as you come closer, he draws you to him. When you are close, you can see the veins in his arms, his muscles bulging. He's sculpted marvelously. I never appreciated sculpture before. When I stand before him, I doubt anything will ever match his power again. I'm done.

A few days later I get to see some of the most beautiful landscapes when I take a tour of the Cinque Terre. All those cheesy screensaver pictures I used to have are suddenly in front of me in beautiful technicolor. Vibrantly colored houses and shops line the villages, and I take the time to linger there as I drink wine and lunch at a café. Although our guide explains how it is easy to visit by train, I am thankful to be on a tour. It provides a level of security I need. It's comforting to have a guide telling me the scams to avoid, as well as an extra set of eyes looking out for me.

The more I see of Italy, the more I wish I had budgeted more time here. The feeling only grows as I move on to Milan and its gothic churches. I'm forced to take a tour of the city to gain admission to Santa Maria della Grazi for my fifteen minutes with da Vinci's *The Last Supper*. My day tour to Lake Como makes me sorry I didn't plan to stay overnight. The mellow and relaxing atmosphere is what I crave after traveling for so long. Unfortunately, I couldn't afford to stay, the rental price on even the smallest villa was out of price range. Instead I take photos from the ferries. I wonder why I haven't known about these gems before planning my trip. Dagobert had me so focused on visiting Edinburgh that I hadn't taken the time to learn about the magnificence that is Italy.

My next stop, Venice, is overrun with tourists as more and more American families start their European vacations. I suspect the Venetian's are either on vacation or hiding in their homes. I wander through the maze of streets with dead ends and constant turns. I quickly realize if I see something I like, I should buy it right away because I'll never find the shop again. Along the way, I find myself mastering the art of a death grip on my new purse. I'm sure I will leave my purse permanently marked with my sweaty hand print.

Maybe it's the tight alleyways I'm walking through that create a perception that there are more people around. But I feel like I am constantly crowded by people in Venice. One night in San Marco Square, I try to find a place to eat, but the setting reminds me a little too much of the place I had my purse stolen.

I hoped to be more relaxed by the time I arrived in Croatia, but I find I'm still freaked about having something stolen. I struggle the most in Dubrovnik with all the people there. I wander the pedestrian-only streets, scanning for pick-pockets between visits to churches and looking for television and movie filming sites. As I spend some time on the coast with a more relaxed atmosphere and less pressure to do things, I feel like I might return to normal.

Chapter 13

It feels like my first day at the office all over again, but worse. I've worked here for years, but it feels weird returning. I've only spoken to a few people over the past few months; many people sent e-mails, and cards or called right after the accident before fading away as my recovery stretched on. Maybe, they forgot me.

Or worse, do they pity me? Should I act like nothing ever happened? Will they pester me with a million questions about the accident and my recovery? Questions I don't really want to answer. Maybe they gossip about me and already know.

When I open the glass lobby doors, the receptionist is new, creating an awkward comment about how I work there and need to see one of the partners. She gives me a blank stare, as if I'm crazy, before looking for a note about my arrival. Eventually she finds a memo about my return and offers to have someone walk me to Human Resources.

Along the way, I run into three of my colleagues who started around the same time I did but worked in different divisions. It's all warm smiles and hello's as they rush to their appointments. I round the first corner and almost bump into one of the newer lawyers from my team. He has an instant smile on his face and says hello. His smile fades when he asks how I'm feeling and whether I am coming back to work.

When I say it's my first day, I sense that something is wrong, though I can't identify it. I wonder whether it's the scar on my face or the limp when I walk. Either way he seems to rush away too quickly.

My meeting with Human Resources is even more awkward. I'm told that my desk was moved from an office to the bullpen on the other side of the building. I was moved from my team specializing in technology to a team working on real estate. Apparently they are shorthanded and need me there until they can finish the current round of hiring. I haven't touched real estate law since law school.

When I meet my new managing partner, I get the distinct feeling there is no shortage of lawyers in his section. Marvin's exact words are, "the firm thought this would be a good transition since I had some lighter projects that would ease you back into our hectic pace." I didn't know how to respond to that. It might have been less awkward if someone had mentioned this transition before I returned. Instead, I feel like I was dumped in a slow unit and they didn't respect me enough to tell me why.

I take the documents Marvin gives me and go to my new cubicle to begin working. The lawyers I will be working with are all nice to me, though I had only seen most of them in passing, never having had an opportunity to work with them. As the day wears on, I see a lot of familiar faces; most stop and say, "welcome back," but few linger for long. Most seem happy to see me, but I'm still uncomfortable. Maybe they feel bad that I've been dumped in another section of the firm.

At lunch, I go by myself for a sandwich. I rarely had the luxury of time to go out for lunch in the past, but since my work load is so light, I figure I should take advantage of a nice day. On my way out, in one of the most awkward moments of the day, I run into one of Dagobert's friends. Clint stops and says, "hi." I see him hesitant to stop, but then he must have realized it would have been obvious he was avoiding me.

He shoves his fingers through his hair constantly, something he did in meetings when he was making up answers to the partners. Then he babbles about how excited he is to see me back but doesn't apologize for having never reached out to me before this. At the end, he just stares at the scar on my cheek with a look that borders on disgust. When I finally extricate myself from his babbling and rude glances, I can only assume he continued with his denigrating glances as I limp away from him to the elevator.

The night before I leave for Santorini, I watch *Mama Mia*, and when I tire of ABBA, I switch my iPad to *The Sisterhood of the Traveling Pants*. In the days before going to Greece, I secretly hoped that I would magically have a package from Eve with a pair of jeans for me to wear there. I mean, we are almost the same size; it would have been perfect. When I get off the plane, I laugh at the text waiting for me.

Text from Eve:
Have fun! I wonder if you'll meet Kostas? Or maybe it will be a Sam or a Harry? The possibilities are endless.

Text to Eve:
I'll take any of them!!!!!

Text from Eve:
Sorry I didn't send jeans. It's summer, who wants jeans in Greece in summer?

Text from Eve:
Hmmm, I should have sent a skimpy, flowy skirt

Text to Eve:
I don't think that would be good on the donkey.

Text from Eve:

I guess we're back to being sorry I didn't send the jeans. I'm
sure you'll still find Kostas without them!

My hotel is simple, yet heavenly. The classic curved archways, all the clean white walls, the light colors mixed with
cerulean and cobalt. A gorgeous pool and views of the Caldera.
I am living in my movie dreams. I use my free time to walk
the black sand beach and search for Kostas and gyros. The
gyros are easy to find; Kostas is missing in action.

The next morning, when I met with my group to sail
around the islands for ten days, there are two couples, three
girls, and two very attractive members of the crew, neither of
which is named Kostas, or Sam for that matter. Our skipper
is Dave; he is responsible for ensuring we have a good time.

The first afternoon consists of learning about the rules of
the boat and getting to know the group. My roommate, Olivia,
is from Australia, and we will be sharing a tiny cabin. Olivia is
just out of college and is ready to party in the Greek Islands.
Muriel and Logan are more my type because they're in their
mid-twenties and established in their careers. With only eight
of us on the boat, it will be hard not to spend time together.

Our first full day brings us to Ios. We have the option
to visit the beach or Homer's tomb. I never read *The Iliad*
or *The Odyssey*, at least not that I remember. But I certainly
know who Homer is and figure his tomb is not to be missed.
Dave also mentions that there are great views and assists us
in getting a ride close to the location. While we have snacks,
Logan tries to tell us about Homer and *The Iliad*, explaining
about the choice between gaining fame or living a long life
with one's family. He loses me after that, but I think I heard
about some long battles.

"Both of your eyes glazed over," Logan chuckles as he
finishes his explanation to Muriel and me.

"Sorry, it's the sun sucking my brain. What's the moral of
the story?" I ask and shake the sunny cobwebs out of my head.

"Watch out for Trojan horses and live an honorable life,"
"I can do that!"

"Now I can live a long life with lots of fame!" Muriel
answers, then high-fives me and we fake a cheer as Logan
shakes his head and mumbles, "always faffin' around."

Later that night, everyone from the group goes on Dave's
Magical Party Tour. First, we visit an Irish Pub, which Muriel
and Logan think is just okay; it's more like a club version of
a real Irish pub. Then Dave takes us to a bar where people
wear a helmet and get hit in the head with a bat. Shortly after
arriving I notice that Dave is missing. Logan tells me Dave
ghosted us, after giving another suggestion for a nearby club,
he snuck out the door. I like to think I'm open-minded, but
the bat thing is weird. I don't have much time to think about
getting hit on the head because Olivia drags me onto the dance
floor. We sing "I'm worth it," with Fifth Harmony and forget
about Dave and the bats.

In a quiet moment the following morning I find myself
alone on deck as we're pulling into Naxos. The crew is working
on the docking while everyone is still asleep. I sit and enjoy
the azure waters crashing to the walls of the town. The coastline is dotted with small cafés, and the hill is full of sparkling
white houses all the way to the top of the town. I'm not sure
whether I am sitting for fifteen minutes or an hour because
time fades away. At some point a tear falls down my cheek,
then another, and another until I lose count. They alternate
with a deep sadness, followed by a sad feeling. A mourning
of sorts, but for what I'm not sure. I sit quietly wiping away
a tear here or there. I wonder where my tissues are, but can't
be bothered looking. I just want to sit in quiet solitude.

Just when I start to feel I controlled my emotions, Julie,
one of the girls from Germany, walks up to me and offers me a
pack of tissues. With that simple gesture, the tears start again.
Julia sits next to me, essentially blocking me from anyone else

who might come up on deck. We sit like that in silence for a few minutes before Julia asks what's wrong in broken English.

"Nothing," I sniffle and go silent to prevent more tears from flowing.

"Everything," I mumble a moment later.

"It's been a long two years," I manage to get out without sobbing.

I didn't want to talk about the accident or how I felt after. But it's somehow comforting to have someone sit with me and hand me a tissue.

Julia eventually points to my scar and frowns as she tilts her head to the left and raises her eyebrows to ask if that's the reason I'm sad.

"Yes, car accident." I half sniffle.

She points to the marks on my ankle and asks, "Same?"

"Yes, it was a bad accident. I'm still broken." I give her a half smile in appreciation while the tears flow.

"You're good," she tells me, pats my leg, and leaves the pack of tissues as she goes back inside the sailboat.

I sit for a while longer, wondering why me, and knowing why doesn't matter. The only thing that matters is that I survived it and one day I will be a better person for it. But it will always be a piece of me, reminding me that I am survivor, even when I don't feel like one.

However, I need to get on with my day. I can't spend it crying on a boat. I'm on a happy and amazing adventure. I wipe my tears, force a smile, and get ready to leave the boat. At least I succeed in not crying again. I do suffer a little paranoia that maybe Julia told everyone about my breakdown and now they're avoiding me. Completely ignoring the fact that she barely speaks English.

Thankfully, the group is lively, and by the time we leave the boat, most of my paranoia has passed. As I become involved in more things throughout the day, I feel better. An occasional smile from Julia helps.

Finally, on Mykonos, I learn more about the most famous of the Greek Islands. Before we leave the boat, Dave tells us to look for Peter Pelican, the mascot of the island. He'll buy a drink for anyone who gets a picture with one of the three pelicans. Unfortunately, we're so distracted by the maze of white washed shops and the beaches that no one finds Peter.

After dinner overlooking the Adriatic, it's time to hit the clubs again. It isn't long before I find myself in a club dancing with a tall, dark-haired man. He has chiseled arms and the tannest skin I have ever seen. As I am dancing with my arms in the air, I can feel the heat radiating off him and sense the outline of his body even though he isn't quite touching me. I haven't felt like this in a long time. The tingle that runs through my body from a man's hands causes a chill to course through my body, a chill stronger than the heat that's causing us to sweat.

A few songs later we stop dancing to get drinks we don't need. Or as the song tells us, "I could have another but probably should not." Not knowing his name, I figure it's time to learn a little about this glistening Greek god who dances like Ricky Martin.

"So, did you say your name was Kostas by chance?" comes out of my mouth with a giddy laugh.

He rolls his eyes as he answers, "I didn't, but my sister loves that movie. I guess you're not Lena either?"

"Nope, but my blonde hair should have given me away," I say as I twirl my ponytail through my fingers.

"True. no jeans either." He raises his eyebrows to my challenge.

I throw my arms up in mock outrage. "I know, my friend forgot to send them, epic fail!"

"I guess you're on holiday?"

"Yup, taking a little break from life on the Greek Islands. You?" I try to sound lighthearted and vacation–happy to keep the conversation going.

He responds slightly-more seriously giving me a quick summary of how he came to Mykonos. "Live here, friend's birthday, got talked into going out for the night."

The conversation dwindles and I drag him to the dance floor when "I got sunshine in my pocket and good soul in my feet" starts playing. I'm not sure how much time has passed when Olivia pulls me off the dance floor to head back to the boat. When I offer my phone number, I find out that his real name is Dimitris. I hope I hear from him again.

The next morning I nurse my hangover on a beach while Muriel and Olivia spend their time convincing me to go scuba diving. There's a piece of me that wants to go, but because I never finished my certification at home, because of the accident, I feel a weird bitterness toward the sport. Not that I'm willing to share that with Muriel and Olivia. I just give them a long list of excuses why I can't go: my ears would hurt, I'm hung over, I'll look tasty to a hungry shark. The more I complain, the more we laugh at how creative my stories are. The laughter distracts me from the real reason I don't want to go. I give in.

That's how I find myself watching a video about equipment, breathing, and equalizing. When it's time to put on our equipment, I'm shaking. I'm not sure whether I'm freaking out or excited at the chance to swim under water like a fish. After entering the water, I have some common sense knocked into me when the tank hits my head. The tank is heavy, the outfit I'm wearing has probably been worn by a million people. What if the tank fails? My thoughts race as the instructor makes sure everyone in the group is ready to descend. We don't have *Jaws* music for dramatic effect. Once I drop below the waterline, I realize there's no need for dramatic music; instead, there's a great calm under the water. I'm still feeling no sensation or desire to rise to the surface. I lived this moment in a past life. Somehow it didn't fit my life then, but it's perfect now.

Oh, and the instructor gives instructions and tests our equipment. Once we're cleared, we can explore in the immediate area. Instead of swimming, I try to bounce around like an astronaut on the moon. Apparently, scuba diving doesn't work that way because I bang my head on the tank again. By the end of our session, I finally enjoy the dive and don't want to leave.

I spend the rest of the time island–hopping on beaches, shopping, exploring historic sites, and trying to convince someone to go scuba diving again. Their refusal is worse when they take me snorkeling and tell me that it's just like scuba diving. It is not! It is so not the same—no peace, all that salt in my mouth. Once I accidentally breathe in after going under water; it was awful. The tightness as water enters my lungs, followed by the coughing up of water while I'm desperately trying to tread more water. I'm still coughing an hour later. I now have a glimpse of what it's like to drown, and I don't want to die that way.

I hear from Dimitris a few times. He gives me a few suggestions of things to do, like snorkeling. I tell him my feelings on the subject. He likes snorkeling and tells me I'm being a baby. He grew up snorkeling. Dimitris talks about coming to Santorini to meet me after my island–hoping tour is done, but it doesn't work out.

As I drink coffee on the boat overlooking the turquoise Adriatic Sea on my last day, I wonder if this could be my life. I think I could do this every morning. If only I knew Greek, I could try to get a job here.

I use some of the free time to read some news and e-mails if a subject line catches my eye. "Danger at the border of Zimbabwe and South Africa." I jump a little too quickly to read the e-mail. It's from Charlie, one of the lawyers who thought I was crazy for taking this trip. "What dignified woman travels around the world alone, it's dangerous." He also considers staying in a three-star hotel "roughing it," so he isn't the best person to discuss travel with.

Since I do read the e-mail, I now know there were recent protests at the border I crossed a few weeks ago after some trade rules were imposed. It sounds like it might have been dangerous for a brief period. I'm glad that part of the trip is over. I also know that I was in safe hands with Sharon. Of course, knowing what the other options are for entering Zimbabwe, I wonder what the backup plan was; as I recall, the other options didn't involve real roads.

While I'm writing my colleague back to make sure he knows I'm safe on the Greek Islands, I mention that I survived the crossing a few weeks ago. As I type my reply, I wonder what made Charlie so afraid of the world. I was afraid too when I was planning my trip and really limited the number of places I considered visiting first. But I did my best to overcome those fears by doing research and speaking to people who had been to those places, instead of just relying on clickbate headlines.

Apparently, Charlie is still working because his response is nearly instant. He tells me I need to be careful in Greece; they are always protesting and their economy is in shambles. I shake my head and give myself a pat for supporting the economy.

A few days later as I lay awake in my hotel room in Athens, I get a call from Dimitris. He is in Athens visiting family and wants to know if I'm busy. Busy? Yes, my visits to the museums and cafés have a very strict schedule of come when you want to. The good news is that schedule fits his.

It turns out Dimitris isn't just a cute guy in a club: he knows his history. He brings the Acropolis and Parthenon to life, explaining there are many acropolises, but this one is *the* Acropolis. He guides me through the museum, explaining about the archeological digs in the area. That's how I eventually learn he's an archeologist. He's adorably passionate when he tells how the British stole many of Greek artifacts when the Turks ruled Greece.

Later, he takes me to a great restaurant, and we make plans to meet in London and steal some of the artifacts from the British Museum. When we bring them back to Greece, we'll be heroes! After we get out of jail, of course, and are featured on an episode of *Locked Up Abroad*. After lunch, Dimitris walks me through neighborhoods I would have been afraid to see alone and buys me "the best baklava in all of mainland Greece." The best baklava, he insists, is on Santorini at his mother's house. The day ends nothing like I pictured it would when I awoke this morning.

As we say good night, he seems to want to say more; instead, he gives me a kiss on the cheek and leaves. We would continue to text from time to time, but eventually they stop. It bothered me at first, but with over two months of traveling left, I focus on the adventures ahead.

Chapter 14

I thought things would be back to normal after a month at work—or close to normal. Instead, they are worse. What I thought would be a temporary transfer to help me ease back into work seems to be a permanent transfer. I know I'm not around as much as I used to be. With two physical therapy appointments a week, doctors' appointments, and a limp that has me dragging around the building, I simply can't be at work as much. It doesn't help that I'm commuting to work from Long Island, instead of a twenty-minute walk from my apartment. It's exhausting. But at least the critical stares have stopped.

It is nice to get my brain working again, but for the first time in a long time, work feels like work. Maybe it shows. It doesn't help that I'm working on something I don't enjoy. The tedious details of real estate are driving me crazy. Instead of being the person people went to with questions, I have become the person asking questions. I'm frustrated.

And it took longer than I expected to find the rhythm of working: physically getting up and going to the office was a challenge. I wake at 5:00, though lately it's closer to 5:30. I don't get home until 6:00 or 7:00 at night. If I don't have physical therapy, I come home and go to bed after dinner—usually crying myself to sleep. I barely have time or energy to pay my bills or shop. I haven't even gone to the movies because I'm so tired.

A couple times I notice the lunchroom gets quiet when I walk in; people stop talking or change topics. I've also heard people complaining about the lawyers who don't spend as much time at work but still expect to be promoted. I used to think like that, but now I know how naive my thoughts were. I also know that I'm not going to change their minds and I'm not going to be promoted for a long time. I am stuck.

I am grumpy when it's time to leave Athens. I had a fantastic time in Greece, and I don't want to leave. I'm also a little nervous about going to China. Most of my trip has been through Western countries; even in Africa there were strong Western influences. I only had basic ideas about China, that it was a mix of tourists with DSLR cameras, poor air quality, and, of course, the Great Wall. I'm not sure where that weird mix came from, but I should have probably done more research.

On the first of my flights to Beijing I sit next to a woman who introduces herself as Patty. I say a quiet "hi" and get my book out for the flight. Once I'm settled, Patty asks where I'm going, and we talk about her previous trips to Beijing. After we get past her advice to take mass transit or to bike around the city, we start chatting about my stereotypes of Beijing.

"All that talk during the Olympics about the smog, I'm not sure what to think about it," I sigh.

"That's true, the topography of the city can make the smog worse than other places. But it's also a bit of story, if you're a healthy woman visiting for a few days, you'll be fine. You're from New York City, and you don't have the air pollution they have in Beijing. However, I bet if you asked a tourist from a rural area, they would notice a difference in the air quality when visiting New York City." She waves her arms around pointing in different directions as she says it. Patty is a very animated.

"That's true, I never thought like that." Interesting theory, and I do notice a slight difference in the air when I'm outside the city.

"It's something that we do as people, tell ourselves stories about things and believe they are true. But in the end, they represent our fears."

"Are you saying I'm afraid of bad air?" I respond, half joking.

"Not exactly. You're afraid of something different, in this case the air, your personal space, and anything else running through your head. But the truth is, it's a new place, a place you don't know and that is stressful. You focus on the little things you're afraid of, making them conform to your stereotype until you convince yourself it's all true. Meanwhile, there might have been other great things you missed because you were focused on the negative." She frowns as she explains the last part.

"So, I'm not going to like Beijing because I told myself I wouldn't like it?" That doesn't sound like a good way to start my visit.

"Maybe you're less likely to like it. You've set yourself up not to like it, and you're more likely to notice the things that reinforce your stereotypes." She pauses for a few seconds before continuing, "When you do like something, you'll probably think it's an exception before you think it's the rule."

"Like a defense mechanism?" I ask since she has me curious about her theory.

"Yes, it allows us to separate ourselves from whatever the real issue is. We do it all the time. Our minds are always running, making up stories about different things. For example, we're delayed taking off. I bet you're telling yourself how you're going to miss your connecting flight and get to Beijing late and screw up your plans."

"What? Are we taking off late?" I practically jump out of my seat to check. "We've been on the tarmac all this time?" I finally find my watch and realize that we've been on the runway for almost thirty minutes. I really will miss my connecting flight. I wonder if they'll automatically rebook me. Oh no, I hope I don't get stuck with a bad seat if they do that.

"Yes, we are, but it's only a few minutes. They'll probably make it up during the flight. They sometimes pad the flight time to compensate for delays," she muses. "But do you see what happened? Once I suggested you would miss your flight, I bet you started thinking you'll miss your connection."

Wow, she totally got me and nearly gave me a heart attack at the same time. "Yes, I did. You totally got me with that."

Patty beams when she continues, "At least you don't think my theory is totally crazy. Now that I've told you this, you'll start noticing more often the stories that you make up. You'll also realize that they're usually negative stories. Don't let your mind trick you like that."

"Thanks, I'll try to tell myself that all will be fine. At least until things go wrong, then I'll tell myself I was right!"

She laughs with me and my recognition of my story about China that I need to stop telling.

As Patty predicted, our flight arrives on time, giving me plenty of time to make my next flight. If I can sleep on that flight, I'll be able to take advantage of my first day in Beijing. Maybe if I keep telling myself how tired I am, it will help.

Telling myself I would sleep seemed to work. I manage to get enough sleep to allow myself to enjoy my first day in Beijing. Before I arrived, I worried about crowds in a country so populated, and although I find crowds in certain places, it's nothing extreme compared to New York, London, or Venice. The people are also very nice and eager to help, particularly with my luggage. No scams, no asking for a tip, just being helpful.

While planning my trip, I often wondered if I would tire of seeing beautiful places and things. Would the thrill fade after a couple weeks? After over three months of travel, the thrill has not faded at all. The Great Wall of China is a good example of an amazing place to see. Although I knew little about the wall, I knew I had to experience it. I learn that it took over a thousand years to build, which would help explain why it's different in certain areas. It's much more fascinating than I expected, with it snaking over the hills of green. Despite the statistics I read and hearing facts from the guide, nothing prepared me for the size of the wall. It's wide enough for ten soldiers to march abreast or two war chariots to rumble side-by-side. The preserved section is the same distance as the Hollywood Walk of Fame. Not that I walked that far. It's not surprising that you can see it from space. I'm surprised they couldn't see it from the Death Star.

By my last day in Beijing, I am almost accustomed to the city, the people, the food, the air, I can even remember the order of the Yuan, Ming, and Qing Dynasties. The air pollution isn't as bad as I expected. At times, I can feel a heaviness in my chest, but it doesn't last long and the less I think about it, the faster I adapt.

My next adventure didn't seem like much of an adventure when I planned it, but as it gets closer I am starting to wonder. I am going to Shanghai, to visit a new Disney park. Visiting the parks at home is such a great childhood memory. I knew that if I traveled this far halfway around the world, I had to come visit Disneyland. Besides, it's on the way to my next destination, Vietnam. Not that I even need an excuse, it's my trip; I can visit if I want to.

I find time to visit the Yuyuan Garden, the most famous green space in the city. Originating during the Ming Dynasty, it's thousands of years old. It survived the British occupation, the Opium Wars, and the Taiping Rebellion. Today it's biggest threat comes from large crowds seeking a peaceful moment in a busy city.

The following morning, I'm ready before the park opens, I'm excited to see the first piece of nostalgia when I arrive: the train station. As I walk under the station, I finally get my first glimpse of the castle and, wow, it's huge! Even from a distance, I can tell the castle has an insane level of detail. I can't wait to see it up close.

I'm in love with the castle and the amazing attention to detail, it seems to incorporate a few elements from other parks, but it is also different enough to stand on its own. As I make my way through the park, I compare everything to the parks of my childhood. It's a blissful reminder of the carefree times with my family.

My reverie continues–until I walk into the bathroom and see a squatter toilet. I stare at it. I haven't had to use one, and even though I knew the day would come, I'm not ready for the cultural clash. My leg isn't ready to try squatting either. I feel a tap on the shoulder and a woman points to the end of the row of stalls where there is a line of two women, one with a young girl holding her hand. Judging by the light skin and blonde hair of both women, I assume they're not Chinese. I hope it means what I want it to mean–that there is a regular toilet there.

I find myself tapping the shoulder of the woman ahead of me in line. "Is this a regular toilet?"

She smiles and nods. "Yes, they seem to have a regular one in each bathroom, you just have to look for it."

I thank her and wait my turn. My whole body relaxes when I open the door and find a regular toilet. After, I wonder if I should try the squatter toilet here since they looked clean. I decide to use whatever bathroom is available and consider it an adventure. Unless it's when my leg it sore, I don't think that would be a good time to try a squatter toilet.

I'm sorely disappointed at lunch when I want a cheese-burger and fries, and all they have is Chinese food. This shouldn't shock me–I *am* in Shanghai. I stand and stare at the menu longer than I should, even though it's in Chinese and English. I eventually settle on pork dumplings, which remind me of home. When we had the time at work, we would take the long trip down to Chinatown to have authentic Chinese food. These dumplings are even better than the ones we got in Chinatown. They melt in my mouth and make me forget about burgers and fries. I've been forever ruined in the theme park food department by this lunch.

As I wait for the evening fireworks, I realize if I close my eyes I could be in any crowd, anywhere in the world. It's all the same, people huddled together, staring at the same spot, waiting. Boyfriends and girlfriends holding hands while they wait. Families planning their exit from the park or consoling a crying child that wants another sugary treat.

As the universe of my personal space slowly shrinks, I realize the world is a much smaller place than I thought.

Chapter 15

1:34 a.m.

2:27 a.m.

At 3:29 a.m., I get out of bed. I'm not sure why. Getting up just brings me one step closer to work, a place I hate. But the constant and restless nights in bed aren't much better. If it isn't pain interrupting my sleep, it's the nightmares, or the desire to sleep on the side where I had surgery and that brings me back to pain.

I stare in the mirror and examine the work done on my scar by the plastic surgeon, but I can't tell whether it's better than it was yesterday. It must be better, right? It's hard to tell with the area still irritated from the treatment. The longer I stare, the harder it is to tell. I pull out my cell phone and take a selfie, then compare yesterday's picture to how I look today. I still can't tell if it looks better.

I turn on the water and take a long, hot shower. Even after the steam fades on the bathroom mirror, my face still looks puffy. I keep looking and still can't tell if it looks better. It might even look worse.

I know I should just be happy that I only suffered a cut to my cheek and no real damage inside my mouth, but I can't bring myself to be happy about that. The jagged line of the scar near my hairline is like a window to my broken jagged soul. My job sucks, I've lost count of the procedures done on my tired body, even after tracking down the best doctor in New York for scar removal, I still have the scar. I will always have the scar.

I sense that my work isn't as good as it used to be. I get a lot more guidance and "feedback" on my work. They call it "areas of improvement," but I know it's a list of my failures. I think it's in part because I'm working in an area I don't know well and its hard to do good work when you don't care about it. I was marginalized from the day I returned and I can't get out of the rut. Doesn't anyone realize that my work isn't as good because I'm working on things I don't fully understand? Meanwhile, I watch Dagobert take on my old clients and screw things up. Yet, I'm the one being punished!

Sometimes I wonder if they have left me in real estate because it's on the far side of the building. Wouldn't want a mad ex-girlfriend starting trouble with her ex-boyfriend at work. And she's got that ugly scar on her face. Let's hide her.

"Out of sight, out of mind."

Maybe that's what happened. They don't think my work is bad, they just forgot about me. Maybe if I go to Human Resources, they can help me. No, the Human Resources people give me the saddest looks. I can't deal with them. Every time I see one of the girls I can't help feeling worse for them than I feel for myself, and that's saying a lot.

I style my hair with some nifty spray my stylist gave me. It adds a lot of volume to my hair, makes it easier to style so that it covers my face a little bit and takes attention away from my scar. Maybe it's in my head, but when my hair is styled like this, I get fewer uneasy looks. Instead of someone staring at me, noticing the scar, and then turning away, they tend to look at me as they do with other people.

If I'm ready thirty minutes early, I could catch the earlier train. Instead, I decide to climb back into bed for a few minutes. As I drift off to sleep I think I should have set my alarm, but my limbs are too heavy to move.

I arrive in Ho Chi Minh City on a Thursday. It's instant chaos from the moment I get off the plane. I feel as though I've been transported to a strange world. There are people everywhere; they're on foot, bikes, motorbikes, cars, and several things I don't know the name of. The colors people are wearing are vibrant and joyful, and everyone seems to be carrying something: fruit, meat, or school books. As I walk by food stands I can smell the lime, cinnamon, ginger, and mint they are using to add flavor to the food. The city is alive and thriving, there are vehicles everywhere. None appear to follow the traffic laws and it scares the bejesus out of me.

When the time comes to cross the street to get to my hotel, I stop and stare, and then stare some more. How am I going to cross a street in this chaos? Do they even have traffic laws here? Cars and motorbikes rule the road with a straight-up disregard for people. Down the block, I see a group of three people cross the street; they just walk into traffic like they have a death wish. Cars hurt when they hit you. I know this. I continue to wait a few more minutes and the traffic never slows down, but other people seem to cross the street without being hit.

I'm not sure how long I'm standing there when a police officer comes to me to help me cross the street. In choppy English, he says just to go, that the cars and motorbikes will go around me. Then he starts to guide me through the street by my arm. I resist the urge to close my eyes, and instead just pray hard and cross my fingers. Amazingly, it all works; everyone goes around me. Sometimes they come very close, but I still make it to the other side. The officer smiles and walks away. I stand there. Did I just escape death for the second time in my life?

Arriving at the hotel, I finally feel safe. I hesitate to go out again, but figure maybe I can avoid crossing the street–like you avoid making left turns in New Jersey. Otherwise, I'll just take some tours around the city so that someone is always there to help me.

The following day on a tour we are taken to a local market, and between stalls selling wallets and shoes, I find one selling military surplus. I look through the mosquito nets and combat boots and find a small box of military medals from the United States. It's not long before the worker approaches me and confirms they are authentic American medals. He seems excited, as if I must be thrilled to buy medals from my soldiers. As the reality of what the medals are sinks in, the blood drains from my face and I feel a little queasy. My mother's cousin never returned home from Vietnam; for all I know these could be the medals he had when he was captured or killed.

I'm angry as I storm off, thinking of the poor tourists he must trick into buying them. Selling them as authentic, but never revealing they came from a soldier who had died here. The Vietnam War is such a weird piece of our history. Maybe this is just part of losing. They guy seemed to be trying to make an honest living with the boots and mosquito nets. But it also seems wrong to take advantage of people. My anger dissipates as the day advances, and once again I'm able to see the vibrant colors and smiling faces of the kids as I walk around the city.

When I meet the group I will explore Cambodia with, I find there will be just six of us and our guide. Sowanna is warm and knowledgeable and stays up late with my roommate, Lizzy, and me talking. Later in the evening I take the opportunity to ask him about the man selling the military pins earlier in the day.

"Copies. I see them selling that stuff since the war ended. They're not real. Maybe in the beginning, not now. The market people are poor, making just enough to live. They know what the tourists will buy, so they continue to sell them." He shrugs.

"Still feels wrong to do that," I half grunt in frustration.

"Yeah, but they need to feed their families too. The people here are nice and the country beautiful. You'll come back another time and see more of it. Cambodia isn't as beautiful, but you'll love it." It's obvious his love for Vietnam is second only to his love for his home country.

The following morning my group of six and Sowanna cross the border into Cambodia with no issues. Apparently a group of Westerners isn't uncommon in this area. On the ride, I get to know Lizzy a little better. Even though we were up late the night before, I realize I don't know that much about her. She left her boyfriend behind in Bristol, England, and she works as a real estate agent. I decide now is not the time to talk about real estate law because I would still like to forget that part of my life.

Sowanna is right; the countryside isn't as nice, though with the rain, I'm not giving it a fair chance. Sowanna uses the time to tell us the history of Cambodia with a focus on the civil war and the Khmer Rouge regime as we head to Phnom Penh and the Killing Fields.

He was a teenager during the Khmer Rouge, just old enough to remember the comforts of a thriving country that was transformed by civil war and having to learn to keep his eyes down and his mouth shut if he wanted to stay alive. He worked in fields twelve or more hours a day, every day. He watched as friends and families disappeared and never returned.

As we tour through Choeung Ek and the Tuol Sleng Genocide Museum, Sowanna explains that around two million people were killed in the genocide, one-fourth of eight million people lost due to executions, starvation, and poor medical care. It took the invasion of the Vietnamese to save them, which explains his sympathy for the Vietnamese when he spoke the day before.

Sowanna chooses to stop under the canopy of a tree with the rain falling upon us. As he paints a picture of the senseless execution of children, we find out the spot he chose was not by accident: it was one of the preferred execution sites. It shouldn't be surprising given where we are; yet, the beautiful tree offers the promise of memorial tranquility to those who died here.

As the day unfolds, Sowanna inserts tidbits of his life into the conversation, talking about how growing up on a farm made the transition under Khmer Rouge slightly easier, how his relatives who were sent from the city to work on the farm had it harder. Initially, at least. Eventually everyone was working on the farms from dawn until whenever; it didn't matter the time because you couldn't go back to your communal home until you were allowed. The Khmer Rouge took care of everything, from meals to health care. This allowed them to spend more time working and reporting on each other. What were they being reported for? Being educated, not knowing their job well enough and therefore sabotaging the system, and, of course, committing treason. Not that anyone had time to commit treason, but if you were being interrogated you could always lie and report someone else to the government. That would often reduce your punishment. Of course, your own children could report you. You couldn't trust anyone.

Later that night we have dinner, and everyone tries to discuss positive things instead of dwelling on the sadness of the day. After dinner I find myself talking with Sowanna about how strong he is after all he witnessed. How can he do these tours and relive all that repeatedly? Although he spoke passionately on the topic, he didn't seem stuck in the emotions.

"At the time, I was young and didn't really understand. I just waited for someone to rescue us. Eventually they did."

"The Vietnamese?" I ask, remembering what he had said earlier.

"Yes. They took too long to come and end the torture. But they came." Sowanna pauses and offers a sigh of relief before he continues. "I was angry after. Just an angry twenty-year-old who only knew how to farm. I waited for family and friends who never came home. I had no future outside of working in a field. I knew I needed to find a way out of farming. I tried different things, and the anger faded, but I didn't have any hope. I just lived."

I listen intently, wondering how he got himself out of that feeling, hoping I might do the same.

"Then I met a missionary. He suggested I do tours for visitors. At the time tourism wasn't that big here. A while later, I received a letter from that friend. He was in Phnom Penh and met someone who was starting a tour company and needed help."

As he tells this story, I realize it's one of the few times I see a smile that reaches his eyes.

"How long ago was that?" I can't picture him doing anything other than being a tour guide.

"Over ten years. I didn't have much to offer, except that my friends said I was good at telling stories. But I hated telling these stories. It killed me a little each time."

Because the smile in his eyes leaves as he talks about telling the bad stories, I ask why he continued to guide. "Sometimes I would tell a story and I could see it change them. You could see in their eyes," he says as he points to his eyes. "I could see into their souls through their eyes. It made me feel better, and each time it was easier to do my job."

"You don't get tired of it?" It seems monotonous to do this week after week.

He shrugs in answer and continues, "No. It seems the same, but it's always different. Different people and different stories. As long as people want to understand what happened, I'll keep doing it. I show people the worst of humanity, and I get to see a better level of humanity in their eyes."

He pauses, giving me a chance to respond, but there's nothing I could ever say that would adequately acknowledge the truth in his statement.

"Sometimes it's hard to be reminded of those terrible times, but I've learned a lot about forgiveness. The anger is gone and now I can teach you about it. Tomorrow we can focus on the country's future." The longer he talks, the stronger his voice gets.

"So, what'll we do tomorrow?" I ask, wondering if he'll reveal anything about his analysis of our group.

"Traveling most of the day. So for fun, my challenge is to talk you into eating a deep-fried spider." He laughs at the horror on my face.

"What, are you going to tell me it tastes like chicken?"

"No, it tastes like deep-fried chicken."

We both laugh.

True to his word, in the afternoon there is an opportunity to have a deep-fried spider. Will and Dave, a pair of friends from Canada, are the first to try it. The rest of us look on in disgust, even though the guys don't seem to mind the taste. Unfortunately, I'm forced to try it when Dave sneaks a leg in my mouth. In my panic, I end up eating it. The leg is mostly crunchy and flavorless. A bit like chicken, not really. The good thing is that no one bothers me about trying it again. As adventuresome as I can be in eating, eating a spider was not one of my goals in life.

The food options are much better a few days later when we have a chance to take a cooking class, one that does not involve eating bugs. Instead, we make Khmer curry and fried spicy chicken. Sowanna has been coming here for years with tours and seems to enjoy spending time with the group as we learn to cook.

Halfway through cooking, the instructor asks me about the scar on my face, and when I explain about my car accident, she just stares for a minute. She tells me her husband has a scar as well, except the Khmer Rouge caused it when they sliced him was a machete. Then she walks away. I stand there with my mouth open for a moment before Sowanna whispers in my ear, "That is a woman who is still angry." I close my mouth, nod, and keep cooking.

The thought sticks with me for a while and maybe for a lifetime. I feel bad for her. It only occurs to me how much different that might make things–if I were scarred deliberately. The idea that I would have been chosen for punishment angers me.

Things are much less eventful as we make our way to Bangkok, a place almost every backpacker has told me great things about. And the place that everyone who has never been has cautioned me about, from warnings about protests to what the most common scam is. Sowanna already told us about the scams and how to avoid them. I listened to every detail since I don't want to lose my stuff, again.

Then things get weird when I receive an e-mail from Dagobert.

> Hey Em,
> Just thought I would check in and see how your trip is going. I heard you made it as far as Vietnam. Pretty amazing. Glad you could make it to Edinburgh. Hope it was as great as we always wanted it to be. Anyway, just wanted to check in and make sure the trip is going well and see if you need anything.
>
> Dag

What? Dag, who cheated on me while I was in a hospital bed and then did his best to ignore me, is checking on me? Something is going on. I text Eve, who doesn't know anything but promises to get back to me ASAP. I distract myself by exploring more of what Thailand has to offer–from floating markets, cooking classes, and historic ruins.

After not hearing back from Eve for a few days, I finally write a brief e-mail letting Dag know the trip is going great and that I don't need anything. The longer it takes to hear back from Eve, the more I know there was something going on with Dagobert.

Chapter 16

Last night Eve and I practiced my speech to my partner, Bruce, a dozen times. I'm that freaked out. He's going to think I'm nuts. Maybe I am nuts. After months of planning on the side, it's time to give notice about my trip, even if it means I'll never have a chance to work there again. I'll find another job when I get back. I don't even know if I want to be a lawyer anymore. I don't seem to know much of anything, except that I hate getting out of bed in the morning, I don't want to go out, and I certainly don't want any more of this stupid job. All the things I don't say out loud, not even to Eve.

I knock on Bruce's door. He quickly tells me to come in and have a seat. He has an uncanny ability to give someone his full attention, even when you know he's in the middle of something important and urgent. It didn't used to bother me, but since I came back to work it unnerves me. It's as though he is looking through me when he does it. Maybe this skill is the same one that has made him so successful.

"What's going on, Emily?" he asks without blinking.

"I've given it a lot of thought, and I know it seems silly after being out of work for months, but I've decided to take a leave of absence, if that's possible," I say in a rush.

"How long would you like to take off and what are you planning to do with the time?" He doesn't even flinch. He just stares straight at me expecting a thorough answer.

I try to hide the quiver in my voice as I explain. "About six months. I would like to take some time to go traveling. The last year or so has been rough."

"What do you plan to get out of it? Is this just a six-month vacation or do you have something more interesting planned?"

"The last few months I haven't felt like I was being very productive here, and the work isn't as exciting as it used to be. I'm hoping to reenergize myself, find out if I'm doing what I really want to be doing." I shrug. "It's a chance to see other pieces of the world, something I always wanted to do but couldn't find a way to fit it into my life. I realized I could have died in that accident and would never have done the things I dreamed of doing. Maybe it won't change anything, but maybe it will get me to see the world in a better light and will help me re-construct my career."

"Emily, you've been a great asset to the firm in the past, but no, you haven't been at your best since you came back. I wanted to give you some time to realize it on your own and figure out what you wanted to do. I've been waiting for this day for a while. I support your decision to go. I think it will be good for you."

I'm shocked by his anticipation of something like this. Was my misery really that transparent?

"When were you planning to leave?"

"In a month. I've been thinking about this for a while and started planning a few things already." I pause longer than I probably should before I ask the question I'm really wondering about. "Will my job still be available when I return or do I need to resign?"

As much as I don't want to be here now, I want to know whether I have something to come back to.

"I'll guarantee you the chance to come back here. I think we'll only know the answer to that question when you are back. If you really want to be here, then we'll do our best to find you a place. If you want to do something else, we'll support that decision too." He pauses until my body visibly relaxes, then continues, "My little sister took a gap year a few years ago and came back with different goals. You never know what will happen next. Just make sure you're ready for the possibility it will significantly change your life."

Waiting to board a plane can be so frustrating, with three hundred of my soon-to-be closest friends standing around staring at the gate, waiting to board the plane. It seems like they think if more of them assemble, the process will start sooner. They become three hundred people I need to limp through to board the flight before the rush of coach passengers. Then we get to spend the next five to six hours together on the way to Australia.

When I take my seat, I notice my seatmate is a female with long, dark hair and is being assisted by airline personnel. It's apparent by how they seated her that she's either paralyzed or has limited mobility of her legs. I decide to introduce myself to break the ice.

"Hi, I'm Robin. Nice to meet you," she says in reply just as my phone dings with a text message. When I see the message is from Eve, I apologize and quickly check it.

Test from Eve:
What amazing new adventure awaits today?

Text to Eve:
Flying in a metal tube today!

Text from Eve:
Ugh, that adventure thing is overrated! Have a safe flight.

"Sorry that was my friend checking on me. I've been traveling for a while," I say as I put the phone back in my pocket.

"No problem. How long have you been away?" Robin asks as she turns her upper body in my direction.

"Four and a half months, and I don't go home for another month and a half. It's good to have people checking on me, reminds me that I have to go home at some point. What is taking you to Australia?" I'm curious what she is doing, based on her American accent, she's far from home too.

"I'm doing some speaking in Australia about the importance of wearing a seatbelt and driver safety." She gestures at her legs. "I wasn't wearing mine when I had the accident and it left me paralyzed."

"Wow, I'm sorry to hear that!" Sorrier than she'll probably ever know, especially if I can keep from complaining about my own car accident and injuries.

"Don't be sorry. I was a cop at the time, and it was the norm not to wear a seatbelt. I'm hoping to change that." She pauses before asking, "Do you mind if I ask how you got the scar on your face?"

"No, it's fine. I was in a car accident too. Most of the left side of my body was broken in some way. It's been a long road, but I'm mostly recovered." I try to use my lawyer voice so she knows I'm okay. Robin has enough problems; she doesn't need to worry about mine.

"That's good. I meet too many people who became paralyzed or have smaller injuries from accidents and think their lives are over. I felt that way for a while. It took a long time to find a new normal. Although there are things I'll never do again, there are so many things that I learned to do differently."

The tone of her voice is warm, but there's also a bluntness to it. I sense she has made it sound easier than it was and ask, "How did you get through all that?"

"My friends, family, and therapist, such an amazing support team for me. When I felt hopeless, they were the ones looking for little bits of hope for me."

I hear her voice crack just a bit at the end, but she continues, "But I learned early on that I had to ask for help if I wanted it. It was humbling, but amazing."

"How did you get into speaking?" I try to shift the conversation.

"Friends, family, the police department. All the help they gave me. It changed my life in ways I couldn't imagine. I met others who didn't have that same help, and some didn't have any hope. They were just angry and frustrated with their limitations." Robin seems thoughtful for a moment. "I used to be a runner. I'll never run a marathon on my own two feet again . . . Well, I probably won't." She smiles. "If I wanted, I know that I could bike a marathon. It's all about how you think about it and making some adjustments to your goals instead of letting go of them."

"I'm terrible at that," I admit. "I keep trying different things, but once it gets tough, I quit. I'm afraid of getting hurt and ending up back where I was before. I don't know if I could rehab like that again." As many times as I've said the same thing to friends and family, it never bothered me, until now. I feel so weak admitting it to someone who does more with less.

"I know the feeling, but you know what, even if you fell and broke a leg, the rehab wouldn't be the same; it would probably seem so simple after what you went through. There's so much you can do."

The confidence in her voice cuts through me and my excuses. "What's the thing you've done that shocked people the most?"

A bright smile forms over her face. "Skydiving. That totally shocked and freaked out <u>a lot</u> of people. But there are a couple places around the world that specialize in taking quadriplegic people up; they didn't hesitate at taking me."

"That's crazy! Please tell me that you were tandem; otherwise, tell me how you landed." I never, ever would have guessed she was a skydiver.

"Yes, of course, tandem. I don't know if I would want to do it by myself the first time, even if my legs worked."

I don't know anyone else who has gone skydiving, and the first person who does is a paraplegic. "I'm glad to hear you, at least, have some fear; I was starting to wonder."

We both laugh.

"Oh, I do. I'm just better at dealing with it," she responds, reminding me that she is human.

The conversation continues for a little longer before we each settle into our own travel activities. During the flight, another passenger comes to check on Robin a few times. It turns out that she has an aide with her, but Robin prefers to sit with strangers when she flies because it gives her a chance to interact with other people. When we land, I offer to wait with her until she is helped off the plane, but she sends me on my way after giving me her number, in case I need a little help navigating through my life.

In Sydney, I turn on my phone and see that I have a few texts from Eve waiting for me, telling me that Dagobert is now engaged to Vivian.

Text to Eve:
WHAT?

Text from Eve:
I know, I double checked. They got engaged a few days ago.

Text to Eve:
Weird. She apologized to me before I left, made it seem like things weren't working out with them.

I feel a little sick by the time I check into my hostel in The Rocks section of Sydney. I know I shouldn't care about Dag and Vivian, but I do. It hurts, especially since Vivian seemed to want to make amends before I left. A lot can happen in four months, but something feels off about this. Dag's e-mail makes a lot more sense now; he must have been feeling guilty when he, too, reached out to me.

After checking into the hostel, they help me book a tour to the Jenolan Caves. The next day I realize how distracted I was when I booked the tour. Our guide explains how the day will work for all but one of us. Apparently, all but one person will be going on a tour of the cave together while one person goes into the plughole.

The one person doing the plughole is me. How did I screw this up? I'm not really listening when the guide explains about the "unique" experience I will have. I wonder what I got myself into. I can't even guess what a plughole is.

It doesn't take long to understand that when I'm signing my life away in the office at the caves. It means I'll be with a group of four other people for the day. Though none are from the tour bus I was on from Sydney, at least I'm with a group. As my anxiety ebbs, I notice the pictures on the wall–pictures of people with hardhats climbing around rocks. Not on top of rocks, through rocks.

I try to keep my eyes from bugging out of my head when I realize I will be climbing underground.

I can't do this! I can barely walk around above ground. How will I do this? I feel I'm hyperventilating. I try to take some slow breaths while I wonder whether I have time to cancel. I don't want to die in an Australia hole.

BY MYSELF!

My mother will kill me! Before I can even ask about canceling, we are being loaded into a van. As I look at the group, they all seem like fit people my age. Maybe I can do this. I don't know.

Our first stop is a warehouse where they suit us up in blue coveralls while one of our guides explains the rest of the morning. I'm only paying half attention because I'm too busy trying to breath slowly. Our two guides must be at least seventy years old. They look fit but, still, seventy years old. But if a couple of seventy-year-old's can do this, I can. Right?

Right?

I look around the room trying not to panic and listening to the instructions. I hear only a few bits of information before we return to the van. Our next stop is on the side of the road, near a hole, without steps. Who needs steps when you can abseil into the hole.

WHAT!

They want me to abseil into a big hole? Or, as I prefer to call it, jumping into a hole, to my death, in a foreign country, BY MYSELF. Why am I here? And how do I cancel now that I'm suited up and standing and staring down this huge hole as the others start to go?

It's one of the only times I can remember staying at the back of a group and patiently waiting. By patiently waiting, I mean praying for something to happen. I'm not sure what, but I'm ready for it. I want to cry as I stare at the ones going down into the hole. They don't make it look easy, but no one falls to their death either. Then I remember that my little Eve doll is in my pocket; at least something is here to give me some encouragement.

My turn comes before the miracle does, so I follow the instructions of the guide at the top of the hole. I get in a seated position and push off with my legs. I keep telling myself to push off the wall and stop panicking or the line won't run smoothly. It is a lot easier when you're not freaking out and your arms and legs aren't shaking. I'm not sure what was more distracting, the shaking or the alarms in my head.

Push off the wall, release the rope to drop.

Push off the wall, release the rope to drop.

I do something like that all the way down the hole. It seems an eternity, and the group claps when I make it to the bottom. My legs are shaking so I find a rock to lean against in case they collapse. I can't believe I made it. Before I have a chance to absorb what I just did, a thought comes to mind. What will the rest of the tour be like inside the cave? Will it be this hard?

The good part about abseiling last is that I don't have to wonder long. We just walk into the cave like it's a shopping mall, minus the doors. Inside it's dark, darker than I've ever experienced. After a few seconds, everyone turns on their headlamps and we get a better idea of what the conditions are. It's a dimly lit area with tan and brown walls, floors, and pillars.

At first it doesn't seem so scary; we are in a large area with plenty of room for the group. However, it isn't long before we come to our first obstacle where we have to squeeze between some rocks. I'm fine, but one of the men in the group has a bit of a round belly and it's tight for him. The second obstacle isn't much harder, but it requires us to sit on a ledge and jump down, which is tough to do with low light and you can't see the ground you're jumping down to. We have to rely on faith and the person ahead of us to give us updated information on conditions.

The farther we go, the obstacles seem gradually harder, and once or twice I wonder whether our guides have taken us a harder way to make it more exciting. To my surprise, I find myself having fun, even if I'm still wondering what would happen to me if I fell and broke my leg in here. How on earth would they get me out? The two seventy-year-old guides are clearly very experienced and seem to be in great shape. But I'm not sure they can carry me out.

"You're going to go down into this section by scooting on your butt. When you get to the bottom, you're going to lay on your back and go headfirst down the incline. It's not steep, but it puts you in the right position to climb back up on the other side. Got it?" says the female guide before she turns to go down the rock on her butt.

What did she just say? I can't see past the first rock she wants me to scoot down, forget being able to see the rock I need to slide down headfirst. The only good thing I hear is that I'll be in the right position to get the heck out of here. The group slowly starts to make their way down; I position myself in the middle of the group so that I won't be left here broken, left to die. Not that I think they would do that to me, but I like to be safe.

As I watch each person disappear, I pat my little Eve doll in my pocket for strength and remind myself that there is one way out. If I made it this far, I'll make it to the end.

It's a little scary as I scoot down the rocks since I'm afraid I won't get traction; however, it turns out that it only takes a few scoots to get to the bottom and my feet never slip. Turning around to get on my back is a little awkward in the tight space, but the guides were right. When I get to the next chamber, my body is in the perfect condition to pull my legs through and stand. If I had been on my stomach I never would have been able to get up.

Next I climb a waist-high rock and join the rest of the group. We are all dirty but happy we made it through. At least until we are directed to kneel and go backward into the next section; it's too far of a drop to do it any other way. I scooted backward on my knees until the end. It's uncomfortable, but I'm capable of doing it. Then I slowly lower my leg down the hole. When my leg is fully extended, I realize it isn't long enough. I am going to have to let both my legs dangle in the hole before I will be able to feel the ground. I reposition myself on my stomach with my two legs dangling, slowly inching back until it's time to drop. I take a deep breath, close my eyes, and slide down. The fall can't be more than an inch or two, just long enough to make me nervous.

It isn't much farther before we find the stairs that were built to make it easy to climb out of the cave. It is a large, cavernous area that is well–lit. Other groups have entered here, and I feel proud walking by them in my dirty and dusty jumpsuit and helmet. I made it! I almost can't believe it. My legs are shaking a bit from the workout, but I made it. And I can't wait to see the pictures that prove it.

Later that night at the hostel, I go up on the roof with my mini Eve doll to enjoy the view of Circular Quay and Sydney Harbour Bridge. I'm not there long when I receive a call from Eve checking on me.

"I went caving today!" I practically yell into the phone the second I get a chance to speak.

"Caving? Like a dark hole in the ground, caving? Is this Emily or do I have a wrong number?" She sounds slightly confused over the phone.

"Yup, it's me and that's the type! I booked it by accident, but I did it, all the dark, tight climbing. Is that enough adventure for you? And I had to abseil into a big hole too. I was so scared, but I did it." I'm giddy as I say it.

"You got me on that one! How are you celebrating?" She sounds surprised but happy for me as she laughs with me.

"Having a drink and staring at the Sydney Harbour Bridge." I can't believe this is me, just staring at a famous landmark on the opposite side of the world.

"So, are you going to climb that next?" I hear a challenge in her voice.

"What? The bridge? Are you insane?" This girl just doesn't stop with the crazy ideas.

"You just went caving and you're worried about climbing a bridge?" She sounds indignant at my question.

"Umm, well, yes."

"I take back what I said and I'm calling you a wimp. Even I would climb it and I'm afraid of heights."

I know that tone of false bravado. She wouldn't even get on a plane to come here. She knows she'll never get called on this.

"Easy to say all the way in the USA." The idea of climbing the bridge is intriguing, but I really don't know whether I'm ready for it.

"True, but I need to live vicariously through you." I can hear the smile on her face.

"I think it's expensive," I whine.

"I'll pay for it, and the undoubtable expensive pictures they'll take of you too. You know you want to. I bet I could book it for you online right now."

She's messing with me.

"Ugh, no, fine," I grumble. I sigh in resignation. "I'll go there tomorrow. It's the closest attraction to my hostel anyway. I'll see what I can do."

"WAHOOO! I can't wait to go!" She sounds much too excited for someone who is not going to climb the bridge.

The next morning I walk to the bridge and book myself a climb in the afternoon the following day, which I'm assured is a good time to go with the cooler winter weather. I ask a million questions about safety and how physically fit I need to be. I'm convinced they run a safe operation and that I'll be the slow one in the group. Still, I think I can do it. I also buy the most expensive photo package because Eve said she'd pay for photographs.

The following day, I'm nervous as I wait for my time slot, wondering who climbs a bridge, other than the Spider-Man imitators trying to make the news. But whenever I look at the bridge I see all the little dots climbing on it all day long. I guess that many people can't be crazy.

It's bright and sunny when I arrive and check in for my climb. My group will have about a dozen people with one guide, and the first part of the process is making sure we're not drunk. No one in my group fails the test, and we're on to the next stage of putting our extra belongings in a locker, there goes my little Eve doll. I'm outfitted in a blue and gray jumpsuit.

The assembly process for getting harnessed seems confusing, but everything is securely strapped to myself. Before we climb, we learn how to work the harnesses in a test area. It's not complicated, but it's easier to understand when you're not standing on the actual bridge looking at the water far below.

Once we start on the bridge we form a permanent order for the climb. I'm in the middle of the group with a young couple ahead of me and an older couple behind me. All four are nice, and we exchange some tips about traveling in Australia while we're climbing. The young couple seems physically fit but the couple behind me is slower. It comforts me to know that I won't be rushed by them. My fears subside when I realize how often the group will be stopping. Each set of ladders up the arch of the bridge provides a chance for a break to ensure everyone is safe.

Once we start our ascent, the wind really picks up and my long blonde hair is flying around even though I have it tied back. I tuck my hair into the back of my jumpsuit so that it doesn't bother me as much. The group stops even more frequently the farther along we go, and the view is breathtaking. Being able to see all sides of the harbor on a beautiful afternoon is something I never imagined, yet here I am doing it.

The breaks allow me to catch my breath, but they also give our guide a chance to tell us the history of the bridge. As we move toward the top, it's obvious why they didn't allow us to bring anything on the bridge, it would be too easy to drop something onto the cars below.

At the top of the bridge the group stops so our guide can take photos and videos of each of us. It's the perfect spot with flags flapping behind us in one direction, Sydney in another direction, and the Harbour on another side. In my video, I dedicate my climb to Eve since she paid for it. I tried to make it funny but made it a sweet thirty second video. "To

Eve, who has once again made me feel like I'm on top of the world. Miss you! Love you! See ya soon!"

When we start our descent down the opposite side of the bridge, my legs already feel weak, but since I can't stay at the top of the bridge, I must keep moving. It's a quicker trip down, but more exhausting on my legs. They feel like rubber by the time we reach the bottom. Even though exhausted, I grin to myself and my wobbly legs.

Text to Eve:
I DID IT!

Text from Eve:
I knew you could! I demand a picture!

Text to Eve:
You should, you paid enough for them. I'll send them when I'm back at the hostel.

Text from Eve:
Yeah! Now what can I get you to do next?

Chapter 17

" I hate to break it to you, but you have too much stuff. How are you going to carry all of this around the world?" Eve is helping me pack, and it isn't going well.

"Thanks, Captain Obvious. I invited you over to help. Stop yapping and help me get rid of stuff." I hope her mood improves or it's going to be a long night. Eve holds up two sweatshirts and asks if I am sure I need both. "Yes, one is blue and the other is gray. I need both."

Eve really makes things complicated, but I don't know what I would do without her. Next thing I know she's holding up two dresses. "Maybe I can get away with just one dress," I respond, realizing she's right about not needing to dress up too often.

"Boots? You're packing boots?" She raises her eyebrows in indignation. "You packed hiking boots? You didn't hike before the accident; *now* you're going to go hiking?"

"Not if I can help it, but the doctor recommended I bring them. They'll provide support to my ankle. It kills me a little to have to drag them around and never use them." I keep flip-flopping back and forth about bringing them. They weigh a lot, and I can't see when or why I would wear them. But if I need them, I will really need them. "Leave them in the packing pile for now."

Forty-five minutes later we have a pile of stuff that might fit in my suitcase. Eve's brown eyes light up with excitement as she proclaims, "I have a gift for your trip!"

After helping me pack for an hour, she offers me a gift? Sigh. "What it is?"

"I know you already have too much stuff, but this is little. Hopefully it will inspire you," she says as she hands me a small box that was hiding in her purse.

I laugh as I open it. It's a toy doll of Eve. She's dressed in red capris and has a cute little doctor's coat. Now Eve plans to be with me throughout the trip. "And here I thought I was getting away from you for six months."

She throws a piece of the box at me and informs me, "I will be watching you." It's complete with her pointing her two fingers from her eyes to mine. I can't help laughing with her.

I wake in an unfamiliar bed, again. This morning I'm headed to Alice Springs to see the infamous Ayers Rock or Uluru. But my morning would not be complete without a jarring text message from Eve to rock my world.

Text from Eve:
I found out the rest of the Dag story . . .

Text to Eve:
Do I want to know?

Text from Eve:
Probably not, but you probably should.

Text to Eve:
Okay, fine. What is it?

Text from Eve:
Vivian is preggers.

CHAPTER 17

WHAT?

Text from Eve:
Yuppers a shotgun wedding because mommy isn't happy.

What? How? Why? He got her pregnant? I can't believe it. Mr. Responsible Lawyer got a girl pregnant? I'm not sure whether I'm mad, amused, or sickened. Dag and I talked about having kids. He always said he wanted one, but he never seemed interested in being a father. Looking back, I think he thought he should have kids but didn't have much interest in raising a child. I knew that I would be a good mother and that we could provide a good home for a child.

I didn't think he and Vivian would even work out. From a distance, she seemed more of a convenience to him. Now they are getting married, and having a kid.

All I can think about on the way to the airport is that I was supposed to be the one marrying Dagobert and having his kids. Instead, it's someone else, someone who moved in when I was lying in a hospital bed. The worst part is that he had it so easy. Dag went from my arms to hers. I watched them from a distance for months, silently waiting for them to implode. Dag's mother was waiting for it too. She checked on me in the hospital more than her son did. I suspect it was because she hoped Dagobert would dump Vivian.

I spend the entire flight obsessing about this. It doesn't help the time go faster. Eventually I get to Alice Springs and check into my hotel before meeting with my group for a short tour to Uluru and to find out if the sacred site fulfills its reputation. It's in this abyss of waiting that I notice I have an e-mail from Dagobert. I hesitate to read it, but since I know what it says, I read it anyway.

Hi Emily,

I'm so happy to hear your trip is going well. As I think you know, things with Vivian weren't working out. We actually kind of broke up.

Then a few days later she called me. I don't know how to tell you this without being a jerk, but Vivian is pregnant. It was quite a shock to both of us. I'm guessing you heard the rumors that we're getting married. I wanted to tell you all of this earlier so you wouldn't hear it through the rumor mill. However, I had to deal with Mother, and she did not take the news well. She's the one who is insisting we get married, that we have to be together for the baby.

Honestly, I think she's punishing me. She's probably right to do that too. I was really cruel to you after the accident. I just didn't know how to deal with everything and I did the wrong thing. Vivian is a nice, fun girl, but not the woman I want to spend the rest of my life with.

That's all. I hope this finds you before the rumors do. Everyone misses you here, including me.

Love,
Dag

Did he just tell me his ex-girlfriend, now fiancé, is pregnant and he is sorry for being a jerk to me, all in one e-mail? And what's with him telling me he doesn't want to spend the rest of his life with her? I roll my eyes. This should be the most romantic wedding of the year. I hope I'm not invited. He misses me? He barely acknowledged me when I returned to work, but *now* he misses me? I feel like I'm in the Twilight Zone.

I'm thankful for the diversion when I realize it's time to meet with my group. I don't last too long. Between all the Dag news and the early-morning wake up call, I don't want to be with people tonight. I spend some time trying to write a reply to him, but find that everything that comes to mind is snarky and rude. Not that he doesn't deserve that, but it doesn't make me feel any better. Some feelings are still raw. "Hey, Dag, you got what you deserved," or "I feel worse for your kid than I do for you." So, I close my e-mail and go to bed without sending any reply.

The morning comes quickly after a restless night. The group is surprisingly chatty given the early hour. Even though I want to sit quietly and think of a response to Dag, I find myself sucked into conversations about travel. I discover that two girls are going to Cairns for a few days after the trip. We'll all be on the same flight out of Alice Springs. Well, there's only one flight from Alice Springs to Cairns, but it's still a convenient coincidence.

Melissa is a vibrant ball of energy with a round face, black hair, and dark-brown eyes; her energy is infectious. She has a constant smile and a positive outlook. I haven't heard a negative word out of her mouth. She's just happy, ALL THE TIME! She assures me that she's just happy, and she makes me want to be happy too. Tiffany is much more quiet and subdued, but underneath the quiet there is an adventurous person. I'm not quite sure how I fit in with these two, but we seem to connect.

We arrive in the afternoon. Our guide gives us a walking tour of Uluru and explains both the aboriginal history and the history since 1873. As he goes into detail about the rock that Uluru is made of, my mind wanders back to my e-mail from Dag. I can't decide if I'm happy or sad that my phone doesn't have service out here. As much as I think I want to know more, I don't really want to. I haven't decided what I want to write back to him anyway. I considered ignoring him, but that seems petty.

As our guide continues to tell us about tourism, Melissa asks what is bothering me. I'm not ready to talk about it, but the interruption breaks me out of my headspace. I start to notice that the sun is setting. Our guide shows us where we can hike if we choose, but strongly recommends against climbing the sacred rock. Two guys from our group decide to take a short hike up the lower shoulder of the rock for twenty minutes. Meanwhile, the rest of the group starts to pull out phones and cameras to try to capture a small glimpse of the red giant and the setting sun.

Eventually I stop when I realize my pictures can't capture much of the enormous beauty that I'm looking at. When I put my phone away I find my little Eve doll and position her so she can watch the sunset with me. We all enjoy the view with its changing colors until it's nearly dark all around us.

When the guys return, we are taken to our campsite for the night. Dinner is being prepared for our group over a campfire. I sit with Tiffany and Melissa during dinner and find myself explaining the origin of my Eve doll, which somehow gets Melissa to start asking about what was bothering me during our hike. I try not to tell her anything, but very quickly the story spills from my mouth. The whole story of Dag, the accident, that Vivian is pregnant, and that I want to write back but don't know what to say. The two are mostly silent, just asking a few questions to clarify things.

They come to the same conclusion I have, that Dagobert doesn't deserve anything from me. Melissa says that, although he doesn't deserve anything from me, I deserve something: to get over him. Yes, he treated me badly, but it's in the past. We're not together; it's time he stopped controlling my emotions. That's the thought I fall asleep with.

I have weird, fitful dreams that night about me with Dagobert, but the dreams are so fuzzy when I awaken I can't make sense of them. As I crawl out of the sleeping bag/tent contraption, the dreams shift to the back of my mind. Instead, I focus on how to roll up the Aussie Swag and get dressed in the dark. I am excited about seeing the sunrise. As beautiful as the sunset was, the area was crowded with people.

The crowd changed the atmosphere. I'm hoping for a more peaceful morning.

I'm packed and layered within twenty minutes and right on time for the trip back to Uluru, a record for me. As we leave, Tiffany makes sure I have Eve with me, and we have a packed breakfast to eat on the way. It's still dark and chilly when we arrive at our viewing spot, but it's not long before we start to see the colors of the approaching sunrise. The number of people here has also risen, though it's not as busy as it was at sunset.

Tiffany is the only one from our group who seems fully awake. That could have to do with the fact that she's underdressed and cold, but I really think she's just excited about having slept outside last night and now being in such a special place. She nudges me with her elbow. "Aren't you excited for this? How many chances in life do you have to get to see something like this?"

"Depends how much money you save so you can come back," I laugh. That makes Tiffany shake her head as she continues to bounce around on her toes. As the hues of the sky slowly start to change, I say, "I don't know anyone who has done this." As we stand there, the oranges start to turn to pinks beneath the long strings of puffy clouds. The dark brown of Uluru starts to lighten as the sun shines on it. The light turns Uluru sienna, bright shades of orange.

Tiffany nudges me again. "You know, if Dagobert wasn't such a jerk, you wouldn't be here at this moment, watching this beautiful sunrise."

"You're right. I would probably be married and pregnant and complaining to my friends about him. Instead, I'm here, watching nature do its magnificent thing. I should probably thank him." At times like these I wonder how I put up with Dagobert, what love or desire could have made me want to miss this beautiful view.

"It's peaceful, isn't it? Just this small group of people here, having an experience in the middle of Australia." Tiffany sounds wistful in her description of the moment.

It's with that comment that I notice I feel more settled than I have in a while. I'm in the moment, with the people around me, living. "It's like no one else will ever know what we experienced this morning."

Melissa wanders over and insists that we need a picture together, a reminder of the beautiful morning we shared. Once the sun is up and everyone has their pictures and memories, it's time to move to see Kata Tjuta. Only a few miles away, Kata Tjuta provides hiking opportunities with its thirty-six domes. When I packed my hiking boots, I didn't think I would need them. I thought of them as insurance. I even considered mailing them home a few times. When the guide suggests hiking boots, I'm a little worried. I ask the guide many nervous questions. Is it uphill, downhill, twisty, uneven ground?

Finally, Tiffany and Melissa promise they will help me get through it, even if it means we have to sleep in the park that night. Our guide's eyes pop out, and he tells us we aren't allowed to stay overnight, that the park closes at 7:30 sharp. Then he realizes they're just trying to be funny and ease my nervousness, and he visibly relaxes. But it's good to know we have a deadline.

Along the hike, Melissa tells us about her ex-boyfriend. The one who promised her everything, too.

"I was mad at him for a long time, but I was even more mad at myself. I'm a young, intelligent, and educated woman. I should have seen through him. Instead, we dated for nine months before I had an inkling of his debt. Occasionally, he would have a money issue, which he blamed on the stock market. I would pay for dinners and activities for a few weeks until things were sorted out."

"How did you find the truth?" I ask, waiting for the juicy details. "I was at his place and a debt collector called while he was in the shower. They told me he was a hundred-thousand dollars in debt."

We stop for a moment at a section where we need to climb over a fallen tree.

"They told you that?" I ask Melissa as I grab her hand to support her over the fallen tree.

"Oh, yes, they'll tell you anything if they think it will get them their money back. I didn't tell him about the call, but did a little snooping and found he had more debts."

There's a sparkle in her eye when she says snooping.

"I stayed with him a little longer and tried to help him. But I quickly realized that half of what he said to me was a lie so I left him."

"What did you do after?" Tiffany interrupts to ask.

"I did what every good girl does, watched movies and moped for a few weeks. Maybe he really liked me and was trying to make things work, or maybe he was trying to scam me. It doesn't matter, we weren't meant to be."

"Do you know what happened to him?" I ask as we arrive at an overlook. The group stops and enjoys the view as Melissa tells the end of her story.

"A friend ran into him not too long ago. He's still broke and single. While it took a little while to get past it, I feel bad for him now. My friend said he seemed like he was resigned to being broke. But that's his problem!" She promptly whips out her phone and starts taking pictures, as though her ex-boyfriend means nothing to her now.

It's that bold statement that makes me wonder why I'm even worried about Dagobert. I haven't even decided if I want to return to my firm, so it's quite possible I will never see him again. Who cares what he does? At least I didn't get stuck with him. He never would have taken this trip with me. He would have talked me out of it and told me not to do this hike. For someone who lived a flashy life, he never took a chance on anything. It started with him going to the best schools, getting a job at the best law firm, and then dating a rising star. It's no wonder he panicked when he didn't know what would happen to me after the accident. I upset his plans for a perfect life. He upset mine too, but somehow my life seems so much better nearly two years later.

I take a deep breath of desert air and watch a little bird hop around on a giant orange rock, I have a moment of peace. I feel like I'm in the right place at the right time, with a cute little bird hopping around and looking at me. I smell the sun awaken the vegetation, the soft sweet scent of acacia drifts in the air. All my problems seem so small when I see how beautiful it is in this isolated place that no one I know has seen.

Along the way there is more wildlife, not like the birds at home waiting for you to throw food to them. These are the kind that don't expect anything from you. They're just busy living life, and you're a part of the landscape. Our guide points to a female red kangaroo grazing for food. As we stand and watch, her joey peaks his head out from her pouch while another small kangaroo lingers behind her. It's a wonderful picture as the three of them seem unfazed by our group watching them. As the mother moves around, the smaller one follows, never straying too far.

When we finished our walk, I'm physically exhausted, but mentally awake. My muscles are burning, but I feel exhilarated. We spend a good portion of the evening with a campfire, discussing our travels. It's not long before Tiffany mentions going skydiving in Cairns, which prompts a lively discussion between her and another person on the tour, Eddie, who had been skydiving and loved it. I don't hear much of what they say: I just picture them falling from the sky to their death. Obviously my own exaggeration because Eddie is alive. The image stays with me when I hear Melissa say she'll go with Tiffany. The next thing I know, Melissa and Tiffany are staring at me.

"What?"

"You should come with us." Melissa looks hopeful when she says it. I feel bad telling her no; therefore, I use a different tactic– "I'll come and take pictures."

"No, girl, you're jumping out of a plane *with* us," she says with such conviction that even I'm almost convinced.

Then, I remember that my family would be really angry if I die doing something so foolish. "No, really, I have no interest in skydiving. I've cheated death before; I don't need to tempt it again."

"It will be soooooo much fun. You have time to think about it," Tiffany responds. She says it with her hopeful and excited blue eyes. I suspect this will be a duel to the end. Thankfully, the conversation passes on to something else, although I don't hear too much of what is said. I'm busy working on my arguments to not go skydiving.

The following day as we finish our tour and head back to Alice Springs, the girls spend quite a bit of time talking about skydiving and, to their credit, don't bother me too much about it. They seem excited to have me there to photograph them. But they do add a little push to get me to go every now and then. Apparently they haven't quit on me yet.

Over dinner the girls start again. Now its a sunrise balloon flight in the area since we don't have anything else to do while we wait for our flight to Cairns. They're crazy. Two nights of camping and now they want to go in hot air balloons and to jump out of planes. I think all the fresh air may be twisting their minds. I manage to somehow talk them out of the hot air balloon ride. I'm not sure whether it's the safety record or the awakening before sunrise that helps my case the most. But I somehow find myself talked into a helicopter tour instead. They're safe, right?

Chapter 18

It's only the pharmacy, and it's only a mile away.

I can do this.

I adjust my grip on the steering wheel of my mother's car and take a deep breath. I look behind me again, then left and right and start backing out of the driveway, slowly turning the wheel to my left so that I can go down the street. When I'm almost straight, I stop the car and put it in drive and slowly go two blocks before reaching the stop sign at the main road.

I wait for a gap in the cars to make a left turn. Easy enough. I can do this.

I continue to wait until there is a large gap for me to turn safely. Two gaps go by that don't seem large enough, but as the cars slowly roll by me, I realize I could have made it. I think my idea of speed might be off and maybe I need to be more aggressive. Eventually, the car behind me honks. My knuckles are white, but I manage to grip the steering wheel tighter. I start to feel a drip of sweat down my face and back despite the chill in the air today.

I see a gap large enough and hit the gas pedal hard, causing the car to jump a bit as it pulls out. The car coming on my right is going faster than I expected and honks at me as I step on the accelerator. I grip the steering wheel tighter as I try to steady the car. I keep taking deep breaths as I check my mirrors, right, rear, and left. I do this over and over again as I drive less than a mile to the pharmacy.

When I stop to make a left turn into the drugstore parking lot, the car behind me honks, making me jump and hit the gas as I turn the steering wheel. An oncoming red SUV starts honking at me. I hit the gas harder, trying to get out of the way of the red SUV, whose driver has wide eyes, an open mouth, and a face full of fear. I take my eyes off the face and concentrate on getting into the parking lot and parking the car before I cause an accident.

When I go to shift the car into park, I feel my hand shaking as it grips the gear shift. The feeling slowly spreads throughout my body. I sit there in silence for a few minutes processing what happened before a sob breaks out from my chest and tears start to stream down my face. I cover my face with my hands as my body shudders from the pain of crying. The first time I attempted to drive, I nearly killed myself again.

The morning starts like many others; my alarm going off, signaling I have something to do other than sleep in this strange bed. As the fog of sleep lifts, I remember that Melissa and Tiffany talked me into a helicopter ride. I've never been in a helicopter before, but I've been intrigued by the idea, even if the helicopter scares me a little.

I find enthusiasm by the time we arrive at the airfield and I am annoyed by the delay in getting up in the air. I feel like I'm on a plane and they're giving me the tedious safety demos but all I want to know is where to find my flotation device, and when can I read my book. Instead, we are required to watch the entire video on the safety features of our helicopter and how to work our harnesses. The liability waiver, as a lawyer I know, I should read carefully. However, as an excited flyer, I casually give my life away.

Getting us loaded and strapped into the helicopter seems to take forever. I'm seated behind the pilot with a great view out of the window. You can feel through your body the instant the helicopter lifts off the ground. We start to teeter a bit as we slowly rise into the air. The farther up we go, the less we teeter and the more landscape we see. The expanse of dry brown land and the patches of small green brush stretch to the horizon.

The mountains we fly over aren't nearly as dramatic as some other places I've seen, but the colors are amazing. The deep oranges are dotted with small green bits of shrubbery. At first glance, the shrubbery smooths the sharp edges of mountain tops, but the more we see, the more defined and jagged the tops appear. Eventually we fly over a small river with daylight revealing the bubbling water flowing over the rocks. In the distance we see some movement, and the pilot takes us closer to see a family of kangaroos.

The flight seems much too short when I notice that we're nearing the airfield we left from. I snap some last pictures as the helicopter descends to prepare for landing. Just above the ground, we start to teeter again as our pilot slowly maneuvers the helicopter on the landing pad. We all start to rip off our headphones and open our buckles, and one of the workers comes to help us. Once we're all out and have cleared the rotor danger zone, we can't stop talking about what an exciting flight it was.

"It was so amazing!" Those are the closest words I can find to describe how it felt, and yet the words seem so trite. Everyone agrees with my pronouncement though. They remind me that they were right about taking this ride, but in the most loving way two girls I barely know could do.

"Did you see the kangaroos?"

"Yes, it was awesome! It looked like a whole troop of them. I can't believe how low the pilot took us to see them."

"Just wait until we go skydiving. Think of all the things we'll see when we do that!" Thus, Tiffany reminds me of tomorrow's adventure. "Emily, you should really come with us. It's not too late to change your mind."

"Um, no, I'm the photographer. You need a photographer!" I insist.

They just sigh and shake their heads at me with giant smiles on their faces. At the airport, we make the poor gate agent work harder than I think she has all year. We're on a nearly full flight to Cairns and we insist on sitting together, which involves her calling two people up to the podium to change their seats. While she clearly didn't care if we sit together on the flight, she still tries to make it happen, and she succeeds. I would have gone to get her a box of chocolates, but by the time it's all sorted out, it's time to board the flight.

When we arrive in Cairns, I have waiting for me a text message from Eve.

Text from Eve:
Where are you?

Text to Eve:
Just got to Cairns. Made two friends in the outback.

Text from Eve:
You should have friends in the outback. It's dangerous there with killer spiders, snakes, and stuff. What is there to do in Cairns?

Text to Eve:
I'm taking my new friends skydiving. I am NOT skydiving, I'm the designated photographer.

Text from Eve:
Really? Hmmm.

Text to Eve:

What does that mean?

Text from Eve:
I told you to go channel Tim McGraw and go skydiving

Text to Eve:
I'm not going skydiving. I could die!

Text from Eve:
You went to the outback with deadly spiders and snakes and now you're worried about dying? Did you at least ride a bull?

Text to Eve:
It's Australia, not Texas!

Is she joking or does she really think I'd ride a bull in Australia?

Text from Eve:
You're not going to die, but pretend you might, and do something fun and crazy that will make tomorrow awesome.

Text to Eve:
I'll take that under advisement.

Geez, some people are so pushy. Why is Eve so interested in me skydiving? Hasn't she seen those shows where the parachute doesn't open and people fall screaming to their deaths? That wouldn't be fun, and neither is dinner with two girls who keep talking about going skydiving. Instead, I steer us to talk about the rest of our travel plans. Soon I'll be headed to New Zealand and then back home. I can't believe it's only been five months. I thought I would have more clarity about what I would do when I got home. I'm hoping a lot can happen in a month, especially during the next month before I get home.

The following morning we're up early because the sky–dive places like an early start. As we wait outside the hostel for our pick up, I look at the sky. I see the most beautiful blue sky I've ever seen. Deep, deep blues, not a cloud anywhere in the vast sky. We are picked up by Rod, a twenty-something surfer type. He's got sandy blond hair that is overdue for a haircut. He's infectiously happy as he tells us that he has this job to help pay for his own skydiving addiction. When I ask about accidents, he tells us that there's never been one at this center, and even the ones he hears about occur when people are pushing the limits and fail. He spends most of the ride telling us all the cool things about jumping out of a plane. He never mentions that part about dying.

Once we arrive, we are greeted by Ian, who looks like Rod's older brother, down to the long blond hair. When we check in, he tells me that I probably won't see much of the girls so I won't be able to fulfill my photography duties. When he hands over the release forms, I take one, lawyer that I am, and review the terms. When I ask Ian if one of the terms is legally binding, his response is that no one has died, so no one has sued. So he doesn't know whether it is. And he hopes he never knows.

"Why aren't you going?" As much as he initially appeared a surfer dude with no responsibilities in life, I see a genuine curiosity in his eyes when he asks.

"Afraid of death. I escaped it once. Don't want to tempt death again." I shrug at the obviousness of my response.

"What happened?" A warm concern is in his blue eyes. He genuinely seems to want an answer.

"Car accident. Today is my two-year anniversary." A fact I had not admitted to my newfound friends. Yet here I am telling this stranger. "Broke a lot of the left side of my body. I'm healed now, but I'll never quite be the same again."

"That's crazy! You need to celebrate. You didn't die two years ago. Instead, you're in one of the most freaking amazing places on the earth. It's way safer up in the air than it is in the van with Rod, but you survived that. Give it a burl."

I laugh at his crazy response, then a thought occurs to me. "Rod wasn't high, was he?"

Ian laughs. "Nah, he's a larrikin. He's always like that."

"Keep him. He's a great salesman."

"Are you sure? He couldn't sell you. It would make you forget what today is. It's really intense and the most freeing moment you'll ever have."

The passion in his eyes that goes beyond the adrenaline-junkie stereotype. I decide to find out a little bit more about Ian. "How did you get started?"

"I was on a gap year in Spain when my mate wanted to go. I was a twenty-three-year-old with no responsibilities, I figured why not? I was addicted to skydiving from my one jump. There's something about it that's so special, when you're alone, drifting down toward the ground. It's like the rest of the world ceases to exist." He stops and shrugs, but tries again. "It's one of the few times in life that the moment takes over and you can't think about anything else and you live in it."

"You make it sound amazing. The only time I can think of that happening to me is when I'm working on a project and time would slip away. Or when I was in pain after the accident and waiting for a pain killer to kick in."

"Those are all crappy things. This is the happy escape, a time to forget that stuff and see the beauty of the world from a vantage that few people are willing to try. They're bogged down in everyday life; they ignore what they're missing."

The intensity in his eyes sucks me in, and then out of my mouth comes a statement I never planned, or even thought about, saying: "Is it too late to go today?"

I recognize my voice, but I don't recognize the words. It's like they've pumped drugs into the office to change my mind and all I can think about now is the view I'll see, the vast view, not just the amazingly stunning images on the walls of the office, but the whole thing.

"Sweet as, I'll make it happen. I recon I can find a discount rate or something to honor your anniversary."

"Really? That just slipped out. Do I really want to go?" I laugh at my stupid question and Ian joins me, "You so do! Now sign the form before you overthink it."

When the door opens from the back, an older gentleman walks in. Ian turns to him and asks about a discount to celebrate two years of not being dead. "Not being dead! Good on ya', take off twenty-five bucks."

Oh my! Did I just agree to go skydiving? Behind me I hear Tiffany and Melissa cheer for me. At least I think that's why they are cheering. Everything goes really fast after that. I don't remember paying, but I know I signed the little slip and the waiver. We are quickly whisked into another room with a couple other people who will be on our plane. It's time for training. There is stuff about our arms and tucking our legs. It makes sense when they say it, but the minute I walk out of the room I can't remember a word.

Next, we are suited up and strapped into the gear that will save our lives. It's a very quick process, considering how important the equipment is. I ask the instructor to check mine twice to be sure it's right. Judging by his chuckle when I ask, I'm not the first person to do that.

I try to ask Tiffany and Melissa what the instructions were, but my mouth is too dry. I figure I'll ask my instructor when I meet him. It feels like we wait an hour, though my watch promises that it's only been twenty minutes when the jump masters for our group come out of a backroom. When Ian enters, he walks right up to me to let me know that he personally picked me to jump with him and that I don't need to worry about what was in the waiver. I manage a beaming smile for him, and forget to ask if I'm tucking my arms or legs.

Ian shows me how the harness works, then we're off as a group to the plane where we are seated with our instructors and given a few instructions about the flight and what will happen once they are ready for us to jump. They slam the door, and it's only a minute or two before we're rushing down the runway and lifting off the ground. The instructors say a few things to the group and to each other, but all the new jumpers are quiet for the twenty or so minute flight up to fourteen thousand feet.

After that, everything happens in flashes. The pilot announces we've reached eight thousand feet. Then Ian straps us together and has me reconfirm the connections. It seems like no time passes before the door is opened, signally that we're at fourteen thousand feet. We lose the ability to hear as the air rushes by the open door with the loudest sound I can ever remember. It's like the rushing of air when you drive in the car on the highway, but amplified through a bull horn.

Melissa is the closest to the door, and before I can adjust to the loud sound, she disappears through the doorway, causing me to scream her name. No one seems to notice. Tiffany is the next to fall out of the plane, and then Ian is pushing me toward the doorway.

All of a sudden I'm looking out the plane door and time stands still. I see the view that is reserved for people with window seats on a rocket ship. I can see the farm land, the city, and the ocean; it's all awesome. Meanwhile, Ian is signaling me to scoot farther out the door and put my head back. I try to tell him I can't get closer, but he keeps urging me forward until my body is suspended outside the plane.

Then we fall.

And fall.

And fall.

It doesn't feel like I thought it would feel. I manage to scream, possibly the first thing to come out of my mouth since training. Ian pulls my arms so they're stretched out at my sides. Now I feel the full force of the wind on my face and arms.

The skin on my face pulls as the wind presses against the bones and pulls at the crevices around my nose where the skin doesn't know where to go. It feels like my screams are never given the chance to leave my body, that they blow back into my mouth as I fall.

The wind on my hand shows me how the excess skin pulls away from my fingers and changes as I move my hand around. My jumpsuit flaps around me, making noise above the sound of the wind as the air rushes by me at some crazy speed. As I move my hands, I can feel the changes in the wind speed and direction; sometimes the wind seems to slow down and then suddenly increases exponentially. I can't fathom how fast I might be going. I look and realize how much closer the ground appears after only a few seconds.

Ian nudges me to look to my left and I suddenly realize the photographer is already taking pictures of me. I'm sure I have a strangely contorted smile as I wave at him and give him a thumbs-up, which is harder than it sounds, given the wind. I'm glad I didn't spend much time on my hair this morning. Although the ponytail has held, I can feel that a lot of my hair came loose as it swirls around my face.

I start to see some of the other parachutes open below me and finally notice I never got that sinking feeling in my stomach that you get when you do a roller coaster; maybe the wind keeps my stomach in place but the ground keeps coming closer.

Ian tries to signal me so I jerk my head around to look at him, I think he's checking if I'm ready. Before I can figure out for sure, I feel a slight pull on us, followed a few seconds later by a jolt, and then we're upright again and floating gently. The sound of the wind as we fall through the sky is gone. We're left with silence as we slowly drift toward the ground.

Ian gives me a few seconds to enjoy the peacefulness before he starts to show me the sites as we drift. There is a level of tranquility so high up. There's none of the noise you find in everyday life; there are no car horns or radios blaring. It's just me and Ian, and even he seems to fade into the background.

To one side there is farmland as far as I can see, square plots of land with different shades of greens and browns separated by roads or dirt paths. Ian shows me how to control the parachute so I can change the direction of my view. To the other side is the coastline and Cairns. The blue sky almost blends with the ocean when they meet in the distance. But the blue of the water is different; varying hues of turquoise dominate the lower half of the skyline. The colors get lighter as they get closer to the beaches that run along the edge of the water. And the horizon is darker in the sky than the edge of the ocean.

As we get closer to the ground Ian takes control of the parachute, giving me a chance to watch the houses, cars, and trees returning to their normal size again. I watch the other jumpers before me as they slow until they hit the ground, while their parachutes flutter to the ground behind them.

A few seconds later Ian yells, "Tuck your legs." I tuck my legs and then we hit the ground, take a few steps forward, and come to a stop. I feel some pulling on my straps as Ian disconnects us. Once freed, I turn around and jump up to give him a giant hug.

"We made it! Thank you, thank you, thank you! That was amazing!" That is all I can manage to say as a teardrop slips from my left eye and slides down my cheek.

Ian hugs me back. "I knew you could do it the minute you walked through the door."

"Emily, you did it!" I hear in unison from behind me as Melissa and Tiffany run toward me with their instructors following. The girls' envelope me in a giant hug.

"I don't know if I really had a chance to say I can't. Ian was pushing me towards the door, and the next thing I know we're falling." I laugh with the girls.

As our group starts to walk to our vans, Melissa yells back to Ian, "Hey, Ian, you coming to the pub later?"

"You bet. I'll see you ladies when I'm done with work." He's got an adorable smile on his face, in contrast to my bewildered look.

"Melissa, we're going to a pub later?" I ask.

"Of course, we're celebrating! Not only did we jump, but you did too. And we all lived!"

I sense her teasing me after all of my anxiety during the last few days. I roll my eyes at her, making all of us laugh.

After sending some pictures to Eve and having the requisite conversation about how I actually went skydiving, and lived, and that Eve was right, I am free to go celebrate my skydiving. Tiffany selected a pub popular with the jump masters for our celebration and in the evening the three of us make our way to the pub for dinner.

Just as we were finishing our dinner, Ian and the other jump masters arrive. Looking around the pub, I recognized other people and jump masters from earlier this morning. I was glad the girls arranged this. You feel strangely bonded with someone when you jump out of a plane with them, or maybe that was just my experience. Of course, it didn't hurt that Ian and I had been talking for a while before I even agreed to jump.

"Emily, I have a prezzy for you," Ian announced shortly after arriving. Confused, I looked around and asked, "for me?"

Ian grabs my hand, and with the other hand presents a small gift bag to me. Intrigued, I rustle through the bag and pull out a tiny parachute.

"A tiny parachute? Is this to remind me of today?" I ask.

His smile gets even bigger as he says, "No, it's for Eve. I heard they wouldn't let you bring her. Maybe she can jump off a balcony one day."

I pull my Eve doll out of my bag, and we spend the next fifteen minutes trying to get it on her. Then we take a series of posed pictures of the doll ready to jump out of a plane and send them to Eve.

Eventually the topic of what to do next on our trips is discussed. Melissa and Tiffany are staying in Australia a few more days. They are both leaving on flights tomorrow. Tiffany has a conference in Sydney, and Melissa is headed to the Gold Coast for some fun. When I mention going to New Zealand in a few days, Tiffany starts to list all the crazy things that she can think of that I should do there.

The three guys are no help saving me. They start pulling out their phones so they can tell me the best places for each death-defying activity. I copy down all the information, just in case, but not much of it appeals to me. I'm still recovering from the high of skydiving. When it's time to leave for the night, Ian lingers behind and asks me what I'm doing for dinner the following night. A little surprised, I simply answer. "No idea. I didn't plan anything."

"I know a good place for dinner, if you're interested," he responds. While I'm wondering if this is a date or if he's just being nice I hear myself say "yes." I spend the rest of the night wondering what I'm supposed to do on a date in Australia. I haven't been on a proper date since my first date with Dag. I find myself searching the Internet late at night for Australia dating tips.

I'm anxious about this date all day until Ian and I meet in the evening. He seems more normal at dinner. Gone is the surfer dude, live–and–let–live attitude I had seen the day before. He tells me that the reason he works the front office is because he's so good at reading people, calming them down when they're nervous and then talking the people who were wavering into jumping.

"I'm manipulating people, but I read them when they come in and give them what they want. I guess my degree in psychology paid off." He shrugs in response to his own comment.

"So what did you read about me?"

"You were a tough one, but I could see a hunger for adventure under all those layers of your Type A personality. I wasn't sure whether you would do it or not, but your friends wanted you to."

"Well, you had to try then." I laugh at his assessment of me. "Type A, you think?"

"Well, you were correcting the waiver, which, by the way, I gave to my boss. He's sending it to the lawyers to review considering your changes." He looks smug.

"I forgot I did that, glad to know I've still got it after such a long break from doing lawyery stuff."

We toast my skills and continue discussing a little bit of everything over the course of dinner. Although I'm leaving Cairns the next day, Ian gives me his phone number and tells me to call him, especially if I'm doing anything cool or life threatening in New Zealand. Before he leaves, his eyes get very intense. I don't have any time to think about it before he grabs my face with both hands and kisses me.

Dinner had been so relaxed that I had forgotten to worry if this was a date or just dinner and what that might mean. My body automatically reacts to the kiss, I wrap my arms around his neck and kiss him back. The kiss doesn't last long, but it stirs an emotion I haven't had in more than two years. When Ian breaks away from me he simply, but forcefully says, "You better call me." I have a giant smile on my face as I watch him leave in the opposite direction.

Suddenly, I'm sad to be leaving Australia and eventually going home. There's something about Ian that draws me, something more than having jumped out of a plane together. It's probably the same thing that caused my body to tremble when he kissed me. I'm not sure how I feel about all that, but I'll miss his accurate assessment of me. Too bad he lives on the opposite side of the world. But if I've learned one thing on this trip, it's that the world is smaller than it seems.

Chapter 19

YES! I yelled in my head as the meeting ended. I had gotten almost everything I wanted in this deal, much more than I expected. My client will be *very* happy. "Mr. Morris, it was a pleasure working with you." It rolls off the tongue with an ease that belies the nerves inside me. I had just managed to sweet talk a very experienced lawyer into giving me more than I ever expected to get for my client.

"Ms. Taylor, I would say it's been a pleasure working with you today, but I think we both know that wouldn't be entirely true."

I laughed. "Probably not."

"Maybe one day I can steal you over to my firm, but I suspect they won't let you leave soon."

I'm not sure whether he's serious or not, but Bruce quickly shuts him down. "Not a chance, Morris! Emily is mine, and I'm not letting her go."

A smug smile spreads over my lips at the praise from my boss.

As I make my way to the airport, I receive a text from Eve. It's a common occurrence, it seems, I wonder whether it's been intentional. Maybe she figured she wouldn't be interrupting a cool activity if I was on the way to the airport.

Text from Eve:
Guess who I met at work today?

Text to Eve:
I think I need a hint.

Text from Eve:
Remember that lawyer, Morris?

Text to Eve:
From the tech case that Dag botched? Yup, sure do!

Andrew Morris is a lawyer I faced in several cases over the years. He had a lot more experience than I did, and he was good, but if you were counting, and I was, I was on the winning side more times than he. I always respected him, though; he did great work and kept me performing at my best.

Text to Eve:
How did you meet him?

Text from Eve:
He brought his son in to see me. I recognized the name and then from his pictures after all your moaning about him. I might have blurted out that I knew him before I realized how I knew him.

Text to Eve:
Only you. What did he say?

Text from Eve:
He asked what you were doing since he hadn't seen you around. I mentioned the accident and skirted around what you were doing at work and that you were now traveling.

Text to Eve:

> Glad you pulled yourself together and didn't make me sound like an idiot.

Text from Eve:

He asked if he could have your number and e-mail address. After he left I looked and his firm just picked up some big case. I'm sure he'll be in contact.

Text to Eve:

> Hmm, I should probably update my résumé. If I want to shop around I need it updated anyway.

Text from Eve:

No interest in staying at the firm? You're definitely looking?

Text to Eve:

> I always like to keep my options open.

I had been thinking about what to do for a long time. I always have the option to return to the firm; in many ways they have been good to me. However, the last year there had been so uninspiring that it left me cold. Even if they met every demand I wanted, did I want to run into Dag and Vivian at work? Did I want to work in a place that reminded me of the lowest point in my life? That seemed like such an unhealthy environment to be in. Would I be able to perform at my best?

I had to get in touch with Bruce soon if I wanted to return. I would be home in a few weeks, and I would need to start earning money. Andrew Morris and his firm were good. I had heard positive things about the culture there, and Andrew had always been very polite, no matter whether he won or lost.

Once I was in Auckland and settled into my hotel, I found I had an e-mail from Andrew, inquiring whether I had time to talk. I wrote back, explaining that I was in New Zealand and suggested a few times that might work for both of us with the time difference. When I returned from a quick walk around Auckland, I had a reply from him setting a time to talk over the phone in two days. The timing was perfect: it was just enough time to research Andrew and his new case.

I split my time over the next two days, most of the time touring Auckland and researching Andrew in the morning and at night. New Zealand seems like such a peaceful place, so far from the rest of the world, even farther from Australia than most would imagine. In the chilly mornings, I visit the museums and then enjoy the beautiful outdoor promenades and parks in the afternoon.

At the scheduled time, and not a minute sooner or later, I call Andrew. The conversation flows instantly, and without even realizing it, we spend twenty minutes discussing travel. It turns out Andrew took some time off after college, before his first job, to visit relatives in Paris and Rome and got a chance to see quite a bit of Europe.

Eventually the conversation returns to work-related concerns when Andrew explains about the new case his firm picked up and mentions that they recently lost one of their senior associates who would have worked on the case. Hearing I might be looking to make a change, he asks me to consider working for him.

My first instinct is to tell him everything that happened leading to my leaving New York. But I'm able to stifle the urge to tell him all that and ask about the case instead. As he explains it, I feel that old competitive spirit rise in me again. I find myself asking all sorts of in-depth questions about the case, and within an hour of talking to Andrew, I know I'm interested, and so does he.

After our interview-like conversation, Andrew sends me a draft employment contract to review and negotiate from. He assures me nothing is set, and I have no doubt he wants me on his team. I print off a copy to take with me as I head out to explore Rangitoto.

One of the newest volcanic islands promises to have great views once you reach the top. After reviewing the hiking information for the island, I decide to take the hike to the summit. It's advertised as being an easy walk. I find I'm not quite agreeing with their rating system as I struggle toward the top. However, the view makes the struggle worth it. I am rewarded with amazing views of Auckland in the distance, azure blue waters grabbing the empty sand beaches. Even with a small crowd around me, it's a relatively peaceful spot to sit and enjoy the beauty all around.

Without even thinking, I pull the contract out of my purse and instantly like what I see. They're offering me more money than I was making before. There is an option for more vacation time than I ever had in my life, not that I used much of my vacation time anyway. But now that I've gotten a taste for travel, I know I'll want to do more of it. The rest of the contract is standard. I make a few notes for negotiation purposes, specifically around sick leave, something I hadn't considered when I first started working. After that I tuck the contract away and look back to some more of the view, letting the prospect of a job fade to the back of my mind as I focus on nature.

The following day before heading to Rotorua via a certain Hobbiton movie set, I call Mom to discuss the job Andrew offered. She's surprisingly and instantly in favor of the change, but wants me to call the old firm first. As great as this offer is, Bruce might have great things planned for me too. It's not until later that night when I arrive at my bed-and-breakfast that I send Bruce an e-mail requesting to set up a time to speak about my return.

When I text with Eve about the job, she's pulling for me to make the switch, but I get the distinct impression that it has more to do with her opinion of Andrew's looks than the job. While waiting for a reply from Bruce, the next order of business is to check in with Ian.

We've been texting constantly since we left each other a few days ago. Everything from what I should do in New Zealand to what we ate for breakfast. Some of it seems silly to waste time talking about, but that doesn't stop us.

It feels like I've known him for years when he picks up the phone. There's something familiar and comforting about his voice and the funny Australian words that sneak into his sentences. We're on the phone for nearly an hour, discussing everything from movie sets to what I should do about my new job, and when I finally ask what activities I should do in Rotorua, he tells me everything except skydiving. Apparently I'm only allowed to go skydiving with him. Not that I would have even considered going without him.

The community feel of a Bed and Breakfast is alive at dinner, where I meet a couple from Arizona. I spend most of dinner getting to know Oliver and Sherry while they try to talk me into doing all manner of crazy activities with them. I refuse the white-water rafting since it involves waterfalls, but somehow get talked into going into a giant ball and being rolled down the hill. Then we'll go black-water rafting, something I had heard so much about. If there's time, there is also an adventure park where we can go off-roading. It sounds exhausting but invigorating.

Once I'm alone, I feverishly call Ian to find out what he thinks of my plans since he is all-knowing in the adventure department. Or at least he knows a lot more about it than I do. After reviewing my plans and the companies I'm touring with, he tells me I should go white-water rafting too.

"No, it's too intense here. I've never been before."

"Have you learned nothing from me? Just because you never did it doesn't mean you can't." He sighs at the end. "But you're right, white-water rafting there is fierce, but it's safer with a group you know."

"Thanks."

"No worries." His voice is softer when he continues. "I just want the best for you."

We talk longer than we should that night, but there's something about Ian that makes it so easy. For the first time, I feel like I'm talking to a man who is interested in me and what's best for me. I never realized how much I needed this.

The next morning I have an e-mail from Bruce setting up a time to talk on Saturday morning, giving me a few days to think through what I want to ask for. I realize that is something I should have decided before e-mailing him. But that will have to wait because I have black caves and glow worms to see.

Of course, the most bazaar part about black-water rafting isn't being in the dark. It's that they have you put your rear end in an inner tube and then throw you into the water, inner tube and rear end first. When they told us that, my first thought was, who thought of this?

They aren't crazy, though. It's exhilarating and sets the tone for the whole trip through the caves. It is a fantastic combination of adventure since we have to get out of the water and be thrown back a few times. I'm not sure whether the cold water makes that easier or harder. There's also time to just sit and enjoy the view as we float through caves. After rafting we get to see the glow worm caves, which is not nearly as exciting as rafting, but it proves to be a good way to wind down from the excitement.

Later that night I take some time to reflect on what I want from my work. When I left six months ago, I didn't know what I wanted or needed; I just knew I wasn't happy. After the newness of traveling passed, I started to find myself attracted to reading news articles about some of the companies I had worked with before the accident or lawsuits in the tech industry. It's what I love. I did it well before, and I know I can do it well again. I just need the opportunity.

Where do I want to do this work? I have no doubt the firm will take me back when I talk to Bruce. They kept my position open and paid my health insurance for months after the accident. I feel a debt to them for having done that.

They provided so much flexibility with my schedule to go to doctors' appointments, lawyers, physical therapy, or just stay home sick. But just because they did all that doesn't mean I have to continue working there. The question is, will they give me what I want? I've already been offered that and more with Andrew.

I spend the next few days exploring Rotorua, including doing some off-roading with Sherry and Oliver through the mountains. The off-roading is followed by an activity called Zorbing, something only New Zealanders would create. It involves my being rolled down a hill in a giant plastic ball. When the worker tells me to jump through a hole in the sphere, like I'm superman, I know my doctors wouldn't approve of Zorbing. The water inside the ball is cold, but once I start to roll down the hill, the water makes it feel as though I'm on a water slide. This strange activity concludes in a man–made bowl where one of the workers helps stabilize the ball. Once I'm out of the ball, he takes a series of goofy pictures of me jumping in front of the ball.

On Saturday morning, I call Bruce during what would normally be his Friday lunch time, which might explain why he seems a bit rushed at the beginning of the call. I start out with the speech I wrote and rehearsed for as if it were my opening argument, a brief overview of where we are and how we got here. I explain that I will be home in two weeks and would like to start working again in three to four weeks. Before I can tell him what I'm looking for from the firm, he interrupts me to tell me that I'm welcome back anytime and that they'll find me some work. He has a short, clipped tone, as though I'm bothering him with all this. Then it dawns on me: he's treating me like a charity case. I find myself stuttering as I forget the rest of my well-written speech and the part where I tell him that I want to return to my old team and work on tech again.

Instead, I find myself thanking him, as though he is doing me a favor, even though a part of me wants to tell him that he can keep his offer and I'll just go work for Andrew. Thankfully, my brain catches me before Bruce can hang up the phone. My voice isn't as strong as I would like it to be, but I manage to say that I have another job offer. I sense his halting. I picture him frozen with his hand about to put down the phone. His tone turns from disinterested to something cooler when he responds, "That changes things."

Something happens to me when he says that. I find myself standing with my legs slightly separated and my free hand on my hip. "Yes, I think it does. It's a great offer and has me working on tech projects again, which you know I love. The pay is a bit better too, but not a deciding factor. I've had many wonderful years at the firm. I never planned to leave, but this opportunity fell into my lap a few days ago."

His cool tone continues, "I see. Give me until Monday and I'll see what I can do for you. You've been a valued employee for a long time, and we would hate to lose you."

With that cliché, I feel like just that, an employee. The problem is, I always thought of myself as a valued member of a team.

The conversation weighs heavily on my mind a few days later, on my drive to Wellington. The ground is damp from the early-morning dew that is waiting to burn off as the deep blue sky starts to turn more azure. I'm distracted and suddenly my car starts to spin around on the empty road. The trees flash by me like a movie on fast-forward before the car comes to a stop perpendicular to the direction of the road. There's a long silence as I sit completely still. Slowly my brain focuses, and I start to look around. My body doesn't hurt, and when I look down, everything is fine. The car didn't hit anything. I heave a sigh of relief. I look and the car is still in drive with my foot jammed down hard on the brake. I realize I'm blocking the entire road and I slowly take my foot off the brake and start turn to go in the direction I was headed before. There's no weird sounds coming from the car, and it rides smoothly. I slowly give it more gas to make sure it's still working right.

Not long after that near accident, I start seeing signs that I'm approaching Wellington.

It's not until Wednesday morning that I hear back from Bruce. He's able to offer me my job and a small raise, but my assignment wouldn't be determined until I came back to work. It's about what I expected after our call the week before, though I wanted more. They had been my base, my career for years; I never imagined myself leaving. Of course, I always had a different vision of my life before the accident. With that, I contact Andrew and ask when he has time to discuss a few points in the contract he sent me. I also remember that after weeks of silence I still need to respond to Dagobert's e-mail.

As much as I originally wanted to send him something mocking, I just don't feel the compulsion anymore. I almost feel sorry for him. He's stuck marrying a girl he doesn't love and having a child he never wanted. I guess it just proves that no matter how much you plan your life, it isn't always going to follow that plan. Of course, three years ago I never would have pictured myself traveling around the world on the trip of a lifetime. I make the e-mail short and sweet, wishing him luck with Vivian.

It doesn't take Dagobert long to thank me for my e-mail and wish me well. He heard I had another offer for work and figured I would take it, that I deserved more than the firm was offering me. It's weird to have felt so much anger toward him but get an e-mail from him that speaks to how well he once knew me, and maybe still does. It reminds me of how much I lost when he left me, but it also reminds me of how far I've come. I decide not to reply to him.

I spend the rest of my days in New Zealand exploring the history, the culture, and participating in the best adventures they offer. Every day or so I text with Ian, to make sure I'm choosing the right activities and being sensible about my safety. It's with his help that I find myself flying above Queenstown on a zip line, something I never would have dared to do weeks before. Ian is excited to hear about my adventures and shares his own with me. The more I get to know him, the more safety-conscious I realize he is, which surprises me since his side job involves jumping out of planes. But I guess the cost of a mistake for him is so great that he needs to be extra vigilant about doing things the right way.

I intersperse all of that with a call to Bruce letting him know I'm accepting the other offer. I never tell him who the offer is from and he never asks. That page of my life finally feels turned. Andrew and I speak a few times to sort out some finer details of the contract he sent me. By the time I am packing at the end of the trip, I feel confident in my plan for when I return home.

Chapter 20

Another morning of packing all my meager goods into a single bag, but this is the last time for this trip. If I had to list things I wouldn't miss after this trip, packing would top the list. The second thing on my list would be getting up at three in the morning to pack; fortunately, I didn't have to do it very often. But at least I know I'll get some sleep on the plane. When it takes more than a day to get home, it's safe to assume you'll get sleep at some point.

By the time I arrive at LAX, I'm exhausted. It makes the adventure of changing terminals even more challenging. I feel like a contestant on *The Amazing Race*, when they get off a plane and have to get their bags, clear customs, and then find the next clue box. The only difference for me is that the clue box holds my last ticket home. I somehow manage to do all of that and make my connecting flight with time to spare. While I wait to board my last flight, I can hear the Red Hot Chili Peppers singing about how life is beautiful round the world. It brings a smile to my face because I now know how true that statement is.

It feels like a long flight back to New York, even in business class. The space gives me room to reflect and sleep with privacy. By the end of the flight, I feel so eager, like a boxer waiting to be announced before a title match. I become that person who is first up-and-ready to walk off the plane when it pulls into the gate, I send vibes that make everyone else antsy too.

Once I've retrieved my luggage and walk into the arrival hall, I find my mom, dad, Jessica, and Eve waiting for me with a giant "Welcome Home" sign. As good as it felt to see so much of the world every day, there's nothing like a hug from your mom to let you know you're home. Of course, they want to take me out to dinner, and the fact that I've been wearing the same clothes for more than a day doesn't stop me from going.

The city and Long Island look so much more developed than I remember. Everyone assures me there haven't been any major changes, just a few things here and there. At dinner, I realize how much louder Americans are. It distracts me from our conversation more than once. And the traffic is awful. While I experienced some as I traveled, now that I'm sitting in the traffic, trying to get home, I realize how bad it is. I wonder how I dealt with it before; no wonder I was so miserable.

Over the next few days I sleep a lot, reconnect with old friends, and eventually make it to my new firm to do some paperwork and meet the team before I start there. The firm is smaller than my last, with a more focused caseload, so I don't have to worry about getting stuck with a bad case; their whole portfolio is so much more in line with my interests.

The smaller office also has a warmer feeling. From the moment I walk into reception they know who I am. Everyone is expecting me and gives me a warm welcome. It's obvious that everyone knows each other and are part of not only a team but a family. There are no angry scowls as I walk through the halls; everyone smiles at me, most stopping to speak to me and get to know me more, aside from my work as a lawyer.

Everyone knows that I've been traveling, which proves to be a great topic for casual conversations and several lengthier ones, too. It's obvious that the upgraded Emily has more in common with the people here than in my old firm. A few people acknowledge my accident and subsequent scars, but none make me feel uncomfortable or out of place: I'm beyond being anxious about all of that. Andrew encourages me to ease back into work for the first week to make sure that I've taken care of everything related to the transition back into the work world.

One morning I receive a text message from Ian.

Text from Ian:
Guess where I'm going for a conference?

Text to Ian:
14,000 feet?

Text from Ian:
No! New York City!

Text to Ian:
WHAT? WHEN?

Text from Ian:
In a month. It's a conference that a friend mentioned and I figured it was a great excuse to visit you. I registered, I hope you don't mind.

Text to Ian:
Mind? I wish I could go with you!

Andrew was right about easing myself back into work. The daily schedule and getting myself to work are challenges, not to mention having to adjust to the reality that I have to actually do work. It seems so simple in theory, but it's a struggle after being away so long. Two weeks isn't enough time to adjust, but I'll figure it out.

It takes a while to develop a routine, after all that traveling and making my own schedule it's difficult. However, once I get into a rhythm, I find myself loving work again. The challenge of finding the nuances in a case and getting the best results for my client is invigorating. It's not quite the rush that skydiving is, but it's a rush nonetheless. I also love sleeping in my bed every night and having a paycheck coming into my bank account instead of constantly taking money out.

A few weeks after returning to work, I find myself at JFK airport again, I'm quietly humming along to Rachel Platten singing "Better Place" when I see Ian come into the arrivals hall. Ian envelops me in a giant bear hug, reminding me of the safe feeling he has brought me in the past.

He stays with me in my new apartment in Queens, located equally and conveniently between my parents' house and my new office. Ian helps me organize a few things in my apartment, mostly so he can sit on the couch in the evening while he decompresses after being at the conference all day. He makes sure there is one picture hanging in the living room, a giant framed picture of us skydiving together. We're wearing brightly colored jump suits, goggles over our eyes, and we both have huge smiles while we gave the photographer thumbs-up.

We spend Ian's extra days exploring the city, from Central Park to the Statue of Liberty. For a weekend, I get a reminder of how great it is to travel every day. I miss it. Eve meets Ian and me for dinner one night and falls in serious like with him. It's just one more reason to be sad when he leaves.

On our final night together, we try one of the skills I learned on my trip. We make pasta together. It's an intimate experience to cook together, one that I never had in my previous relationships. Navigating through the kitchen together is almost like a dance. We coordinate our tasks and try to stay out of each other's way. It ends with a romantic dinner and I feel incredibly connected to him by the end of his visit.

The following morning is emotional when we say goodbye. There are no declarations of love, but a promise to see each other again as we embrace. On my way out of the airport, I wave to a random plane that I'm sure isn't his, I wonder how things will turn out. Neither of us seems interested in moving. I've settled into a new job, and Ian isn't much of a city person.

We'll talk and visit often for now. We'll figure out the next step when we are ready.

That's the fun of life. We can plan it as much as we want, but sometimes life has a different plan. When we take a chance with changes, new opportunities to grow present themselves and a new horizon can open to us. My life changed immeasurably in a moment. It took two years and a trip around the world to find a new path for me, and this time I'm no longer afraid.

Acknowledgements

For several years, I thought about writing a book. The ideas for that book changed over the years, but the desire stuck with me. At the end of 2015, when I felt myself drifting along but experiencing a strange pull to do something different, I made the commitment to write a book. Within weeks, the opportunity to join Author Academy Elite was offered. Thank you to Tiana Galarza for pushing me to take the opportunity instead of telling me I was crazy.

There are no words that can express my gratitude to Kary Oberbrunner for believing in me and coaching me through the process for the next year and a half. Kary introduced me to a group of authors who are amazing, inspiring, and keep me going each week. Jim Akers, thank you for including me in your launch and always checking in on me in subtle ways. It means a lot to me. Melanie, thank you for our time outside of the conference to discuss books and life, and to help me keep accountable for my goals. For all the other authors who went before me, thank you for letting me learn from you.

Debra Anastasia, thank you for introducing me to the Word Count Crunch. Just when I thought I was getting the hang of writing each day, the authors in that group taught me new lessons in getting words on paper. Sylvain Reynard, thank you for your positive and inspiring posts each day. Just when I was about to let the negative vibe on social media get to me, I would see one of your posts and be encouraged.

To all the people I traveled a part of the word with, your essence is in each page of this book: the stories you shared, the experiences we had, and the lessons you taught me. This book couldn't have been written without you.

Thank you to Sara, who for my fortieth birthday, sent me a little rubber Wonder Woman doll. The doll stared at me for weeks while I wrote and eventually became the inspiration for the Eve doll. Christine, Mandy, Aviva, Rachel, and Nellie thank you for your help with random questions about locations and language. I have no doubt it helped make the story more authentic. Greg Hodge and I had a fantastic evening together doing my cover photo, not only did he take amazing photos, he was also a gentleman keeping me safe when I climbed on the rocks. Without Patrick, Elsa, and Julie, my editors, I would still be editing and confused over tenses. I couldn't have done this without them.

Last, but never least, thank you to my friends who checked in on me but never pushed me: Margaret, Vanessa, Tara, Andrea, Terye, Veronica. Thank you for your cheerleading, faith, and patience.

About the Author

Christine Maier is a new author, longtime writer, blogger, and photographer. She was born with a cleft lip and palate and had enough surgeries to stop counting. Growing up with a learning disability, she never imagined writing a book until she developed reading and writing skills in adulthood. In high school, she fell in love with reading and then wrote some short

©2017 Greg Hodge Photography

stories, and in the process learned she had a knack of writing.

Christine earned her bachelor's degree from Penn State, and later her MA from the University at Albany. After college, Christine took her first weeklong vacation, a tour through California, and was bitten by the travel bug. Since then, she's traveled around the world, including Australia, the Galapagos Islands, Russia, and South Africa. Today she resides on Long Island in New York, where she can be found pursuing her interests: reading, writing, photography, and planning her next trip. Connect with Christine at:

TheChristineMaier.com
Twitter @Travelingiraffe
Instagram @Travelingiraffe
Facebook: ChristineMaierAuthor

CPSIA information can be obtained
at www.ICGtesting.com
Printed in the USA
LVHW100756210120
644245LV00009B/132/J

9 781640 850361